BLOOD, SWEAT, AND CHEERS:
A COMEDY ABOUT COMPETITIVE CHEERLEADING

A full-length comedy by
Kaci Beeler and Amy Gentry

www.youthplays.com
info@youthplays.com
424-703-5315

COPYRIGHT RULES TO REMEMBER

CAST OF CHARACTERS

JAMES KOWALSKI, 17. June's best friend and boy-next-door.

JUNE DAVIS, 17. Our misguided heroine.

BARBARA DAVIS, June's 40-something mother. A worrier who means well.

BOB DAVIS, June's middle-aged father. He's a little clueless but he's got a good heart.

COACH JASON FLIPP, half of the Austin Cheer Depot coaching duo. A bit effeminate and flighty.

COACH KATHERINE PEPPER, the other half of the duo. Strong-willed and sharp of tongue.

SAMANTHA ROGERS (SAM), 18. Cheer, whatever. She's got it all figured out.

GABRIELLA ROMERO (GABI), 17. An alternative overachiever. Lighthearted.

CHRISSY MCCARTHY, 16. A kind-hearted and sloppy softie.

KENNEDY CAMPBELL, 17. The queen bee of cheer with a real stinger.

ACD CHEERLEADERS, various. Ages can be anywhere from 12 to 18, boys and girls. Eight extra cheerleaders are mentioned by name in the script but there could be as few as five.

This cast can include nearly unlimited support characters for the members of the ACD Senior 5 team (in the 2013 Austin production there were nine additional pre-teen and teen roles. A few mentioned in the script are Tyler, Genevieve, McKenna, Lexi, Cassidy Clay, Cassidy Seymour, Fiona, and Kendra).

The fundraising scene can also feature other "adult" or kid characters in attendance that are not mentioned in the script.

SETTING

The setting is contemporary Austin, Texas, specifically the years 2012-2013.

The stage is set with a large cheer mat. It takes up most of the floor space, especially in the middle of the room. It is moved back several feet from the audience to make a path in front, and there is space on either side of it. Many colorful banners hang from the ceiling and along the walls with the years and names of cheer competitions. Several trophies sit gleaming in a focal point. This is the backdrop for the entire show, even though there are several scenes that do not technically take place in the cheer gym. In the original production, alternative locations were indicated with accent pieces to make the transitions simpler.

PRODUCTION NOTES

The original production was staged in Austin, Texas, in 2013 using a playwriting and staging practice developed by The New Colony theater company in Chicago, Illinois. Improvisation was used during the scriptwriting process and throughout the rehearsals and performances in order to keep the acting and dialogue fresh. The co-playwrights of this script are very open to actors changing phrasing in order to make dialogue sound more natural for each performer as long as the meaning is the same.

The script has some strong language, but where applicable there are alternate word choices provided in [brackets].

The athleticism of the cheerleaders was a strong focal point of the 2013 production in Austin, and many of the actors trained for months in order to cheer in the All-Star style alongside the real cheerleaders from Austin Cheer Factory. Many of the scenes have dance transitions and often the cheerleaders do light training during the gym scenes, with the final number being an actual competition-length routine. This is not necessary for the production's enjoyment or success, and can be added in, left out, or executed to fit the skill level of the producing ensemble. There are notes throughout the script offering staging suggestions for each instance that includes physical cheering or movement.

It is a good idea to keep in mind that adding in dances and routines will lengthen the production running time.

ACKNOWLEDGEMENTS

Original cast and crew from the 2013 world premiere:

James Kowalski – Alex Dobrenko

June Davis – Kaci Beeler

Barbara Davis – Jessica Arjet

Bob Davis – Paul Normandin

Coach Jason Flipp – Curtis Luciani

Coach Katherine Pepper – Amy Gentry

Samantha Rogers (Sam) – Courtney Hopkin

Gabriella Romero (Gabi) – Karen Jane DeWitt

Chrissy McCarthy – Kayla Lane Freeman

Kennedy Campbell – Halyn Lee Erickson

Director – Roy Janik

Producer – Kaci Beeler

Stage Manager – Tina Van Winkle

Lighting Design – Brigette Hutchison

Costumes – Courtney Hopkin

ACT I

SCENE 1

(Lights up on a teenage boy, JAMES KOWALSKI, and girl, JUNE DAVIS, wearing street clothes and carrying backpacks. They walk down a neighborhood sidewalk, laughing carelessly and happily.)

JAMES: No, dude, I would never live there! You know I don't like the cold. If I went to any other state for college, it would be California or something.

JUNE: I can totally see that, except in my head you're sitting on a beach somewhere and missing class.

JAMES: Exactly! *(Laughing:)* See, that's why I don't even think I should bother to apply. I'm not sure that's where I want to be...college. I want a job. I want to move out of my parents' house as soon as possible.

JUNE: Oh, James! That reminds me! I have something for you.

(She rummages around in her backpack and pulls out a DVD case.)

The one, the only — Space Jam!

JAMES: Dude! What?! It's been forever since we watched this!

(They both sing the theme song, "Everybody get up, it's time to jam now..." [etc.] and laugh. They mime passing a basketball to each other and slam-dunking the ball.)

JUNE: I found it in the back of my closet and immediately thought of you!

JAMES: We must have watched this a hundred times when we were kids.

JUNE: Enough to scratch the shit [crap] out of that DVD. It still plays, though.

JAMES: If I remember correctly, YOU were always the one who insisted on watching it...

(They laugh and June playfully pushes James, which makes him appear even happier.)

JUNE: NO WAY! You were the one who liked basketball and Bugs Bunny. I was just indulging you...

(The center spot fades and a stage left spot comes up to reveal June's parents: a middle-aged man, BOB DAVIS, and 40-something woman, BARBARA DAVIS. Barbara and Bob clean up around a messy dresser in June's bedroom. There are clothes, shoes, nail polish, random photos, cards, and mementos scattered about on top of the dresser and on the floor.)

BARBARA: I thought I told her to clean up her room or she couldn't go out on Saturday!

(Barbara picks up clothes and puts them in a laundry hamper.)

BOB: Well, June didn't actually go anywhere on Saturday...remember? I was here all evening and I think she only came out to gulp down her food and talk to James on the porch.

BARBARA: I thought I said James couldn't come over, either!

BOB: Well, he was on the porch...

BARBARA: Bob, we talked about this. We have to be more...firm. She's getting older. She's not our little girl anymore.

BOB: Clearly. But I don't think it's a good idea for us to keep her from her friends, Barb. And when was the last time that she had any other girls over? The only time I even glimpse her smile is when James is around.

BARBARA: I'm just worried about her. I wonder if we're doing the right things. Oh...look.

(The edge of a small cheer uniform sticks out of a dresser drawer. Barbara opens the drawer farther to pull it out. She holds up the very small top.)

BOB: That was from her first year cheerleading. She was so excited the first time she put it on.

BARBARA: Aw, I remember that. Feels like it was just yesterday I was washing it in the kitchen sink because June was afraid it might shrink if I put it in the washing machine.

BOB: Better safe than sorry, she said. She was so determined to look perfect then, even as an eight-year-old. I didn't know she still had all of these uniforms...

(They open the drawer farther and discover a small notebook marked "PRIVATE" that they've never seen before. Barbara pulls it out and hesitates for a moment before opening it.)

(We cut back to June and James at center stage.)

JAMES: Hey, Junebug, can I crash at your place tonight? At least until 10 PM or so? My mom's gonna be home late from work and we can watch the movie and pretend to do homework...

JUNE: You know I really, really want you to come over, right?

JAMES: Do I have to stay on the porch again?

JUNE: Hah! Maybe...I still haven't cleaned my room. Actually, I don't think you can come over at all...I have to have dinner with my parents tonight. At the table. No iPhone. No distractions. That's what my mom said anyway. I can still practice turning my brain off like in Biology. Sleep with my eyes open.

JAMES: Do you still want to chat online tonight? Late?

JUNE: Of course! I was thinking you could watch *Space Jam* in the meantime and tell me if it still holds up.

JAMES: As well-written and visually stunning as *Space Jam* is...it's probably not distracting enough.

(He looks sad for a moment.)

JUNE: Hey! I'll see you outside school tomorrow, no worries. Just practice turning your brain off.

(They quickly hug. And then to counteract the tender moment James and June try to knock each other off their feet [or some other playful and platonic combat]. June wins.)

I'm still stronger than you, Jamie.

(James begins to tickle her.)

JAMES: But I know your weakness!

JUNE: *(Uncontrollably laughing:)* Stop! I'm gonna be late!

(Lights fade on the center of the stage and back up on Bob and Barbara on stage left. The parents, at the kitchen table, read the journal they found.)

(Possibly VO offstage:) "Dear Freaking Lifeless Piece of Paper. I'm writing to you because I don't know if I could say this stuff aloud to anyone. James would be too worried about me. My parents are...eh, my parents. They don't know or care about half the shit [crap, stuff] I do. For all they know, James and I huff spray paint and have unprotected sex under the bleachers every day after school. Ew, I can't believe I just wrote that about James. Rewind, erase. But seriously, my parents are so deluded they think James is my boyfriend and we're going to go to the big homecoming game together, or whatever high school couples do in movies. I guess it's better than them

knowing the truth about me: he's honestly my only friend, because I am too pathetic to have friends at school, and anyway everyone at school is so shallow it kills me. GAH! And now I feel like Holden Caulfield. Stupid. *(Beat.)* Honestly, the truth is..."

(By this point June has settled into the chair between her parents, looking annoyed beyond belief.)

BOB: *(Reading from diary:)* "The truth is I'm so bored, I just want to blow my...my effing brains out."

JUNE: Unbelievable. No, go ahead and read my diary, guys. Great parenting.

BARBARA: June, this is completely unacceptable.

BOB: We're worried about you.

JUNE: Be worried about yourselves if your lives are so lame you have to get your kicks from my *private journal.*

BARBARA: Young lady I do not think you realize how serious this situation is. That's just what we're worried about! You used to do so much stuff, June. Now you're so bored you...? I can't even say it.

JUNE: I didn't actually mean it! Mom, you're an English teacher. It's poetic language!

BARBARA: Regardless of how you meant it, your father and I see this as a cry for help.

JUNE: A cry for...you have to be kidding me! I'm done here.

(June moves to get up from the table.)

BOB: STAY!

(June is surprised by her father's raised voice and sits back down.)

BARBARA: I know when all this started.

BOB: You used to be so sweet, so helpful when you were younger.

JUNE: So what, you're going to put me in therapy or something?

BARBARA: Since you apparently took the long way home from school, we had time to talk it over.

BOB: You have two choices—private school or ACD.

JUNE: Wait...what?

BARBARA: Private school or ACD.

JUNE: I heard you! Just...ACD? Austin Cheer Depot? I knew you guys were still obsessed with All-Star Cheerleading, but please!

BARBARA: Honey, we're not obsessed.

BOB: We do keep up our contributions to the Champions Fund. Some of those girls can't afford full tuition.

JUNE: And you go to competitions?

BARBARA: We tag along with the Rogers or the Romeros once in a while. It's fun! I'm still friends with the other moms, June. I like keeping up with their girls' accomplishments.

JUNE: Yeah, I bet. What do you tell them about me?

BARBARA: That's not the point! Don't turn this around on us. The point is, you need a major change in your life. You've proven you can't handle your own time, June. Your father and I don't want to be...those parents. *(Fighting back tears:)* The ones who talk about how they didn't notice what was going on until it was too late!

JUNE: Mom! You're taking this way out of hand. I might be...ambitionless or awkward or unhappy...but I'm not a psycho! Plus, I don't even think ACD will have me back.

(Lights fade down on stage left and up on stage right. COACH JAY/JASON FLIPP and COACH KAY/KATHARINE PEPPER are in their office in the ACD Cheer Gym complex. Coach Jay holds up bows for comparison at a table while Coach Kay drinks a Coke Zero and paces.)

COACH JAY: I just feel like purple is too royal...you know what I mean? It was the color of the neck ribbon on the Limited Edition Princess Di Beanie Baby Bear and I always think of that when I see a purple bow —

COACH KAY: We didn't make a mistake, did we?

COACH JAY: Going with satin instead of grosgrain?

COACH KAY: I'm not talking about your flippin' bows, Jason! I mean, telling June Davis's parents she could come back and be on the senior level five team.

(Coach Jay moves to take Coach Kay by the shoulders and stop her pacing.)

COACH JAY: Katharine, you wear the frown of a woman who has not been thinking of her Success Pyramid, but rather her Destructive Cube. What do we say when we lose sight of our goals?

COACH KAY: *(She takes a deep breath.)* Power is about angles. Power is about being heavy on the bottom and light on the top —

COACH JAY: Exactly. Don't overthink it. When we first met at that *(Pronounced: "power puh-puh-puh":)* PowerPPP self-help seminar in Albuquerque 12 years ago, I never would have thought we'd make it this far. But our combined expertise, me with my failed gymnastics career and you with your mannish charisma and a double major in Physical Education and Business, makes us a surprisingly effective match to run our cheer empire. Plus, what do we have to lose? The senior team looks as pathetic as a bunch of out of work Disney employees. And June Davis was once pretty remarkable...

COACH KAY: True. But two years is a long time off, no matter who you are. *(Beat.)* At least her parents are going to pay three times the tuition rate.

COACH JAY: We started this business to mold champions.

COACH KAY: And make a living doing what we know best.

COACH JAY: At Austin Cheer Depot, we don't make mistakes. We make miracles.

COACH KAY: Cheer miracles.

COACH JAY AND COACH KAY: Cheeracles.

COACH KAY: I like the red bows.

COACH JAY: Yes!

(Lights fade out on stage right and up on stage left where June and her parents are still at the dinner table where we left them.)

JUNE: They said YES?

BOB: Of course they did! You were the best!

JUNE: The keyword here is "were," Dad! Now I'm nobody. All the girls are gonna hate me for doing this. I left right before Worlds.

BARBARA: St. Mary's has a nice track team.

JUNE: I am NOT going to a private school! It's my senior year! I can't do that to James and I don't want to start over with another pack of teenage idiots.

BOB: Then you've decided?

(Beat.)

JUNE: Why me? *(She sighs.)* Fine. I pick ACD. I pick giant bows, ugly white shoes, and fitting in instead of standing out. Happy?

BOB: You're gonna love it again, we know it.

(BAM! The stage explodes with bright lights and loud music and a cheer gym appears, complete with the Austin Cheer Depot Senior Team [FULL CHEER ENSEMBLE] in training. They do a short part of a routine or stunts set to music or they have just "finished" a routine, if one has not been choreographed. [Optional: Hand-painted poster boards bearing the words "BLOOD" "SWEAT," "& CHEERS" are held aloft at some point during the sequence.])

SCENE 2

(Coach Kay enters.)

COACH KAY: ENOUGH!!! I've HAD it!! Can the music, Jay!

COACH JAY: *(Off:)* With pleasure.

(Suddenly, without notice to the team, the music is cut off. Coach Jay walks on as the team breaks, catching their breath and waiting nervously for the shit to hit the fan.)

COACH KAY: This is the most goddamn disgraceful piece of half-assed, broken-down, god-forsaken, half-assed—half-assery I have EVER seen! [This is the most disgusting, disgraceful, disappointing, unwatchable piece of amateur filth I have EVER seen!] *GET OUT OF MY GYM YOU PIECES OF SHIT [CRAP]!!*

COACH JAY: Katherine.

COACH KAY: Not now Jay!

COACH JAY: Katherine, what did we talk about?

COACH KAY: Are you even SEEING this shit [crap, dung, filth] Jay? They're feeding us shit on a platter, Jay. Fresh, steaming shit.

COACH JAY: Language, Katherine. Remember the parents' meeting. We use our language as a surgeon's knife, not as the cudgel of a deranged murderer.

(Coach Kay walks among them, points in their faces, and pokes when necessary.)

COACH KAY: Genevieve Saenz! Your arms look like spaghetti and your legs look like string cheese. Drop and give me 50. McKenna! Your thigh stand is giving me nightmares. Do us all a favor and break a leg already so I can bring Ashley up from Level Four to take your spot. Samantha Rogers! Sam,

I expect more from you. Do I need to call mommy and tell her the champion gene skipped a generation?

SAM: Good luck with that, she's in Belize.

COACH KAY: What was that?

SAM: I said she's in Belize. She's picking out new furniture for the backyard—

COACH KAY: Watch it, princess. At home you may be a legacy, but around here you're only as good as your base work, got it? *(Moving on:)* And Gabi?

GABI: Yes Coach?

COACH KAY: Get your mind out of your boyfriend's Range Rover and back in this gym. Oh, and if you're planning to get any more tattoos, do me a favor?

GABI: Yes, Coach?

COACH KAY: Get 'em where the sun don't shine. You look like a billboard for a trailer park.

(*She steps out in front of the group.*)

Ladies, I am literally afraid to go to sleep at night because I might dream about you and puke and then choke on my own vomit.

COACH JAY: Now, Kay. Let's use our angle of purpose to focus our eye of compassion.

COACH KAY: *(Breathes deeply.)* Take over, Jay. I'm done here.

COACH JAY: Girls. No—young women *(Beat.)* and Tyler. Coach Kay looks at you, and she sees shit [or whatever word was used earlier]. I look at you, and I see—well, I see shit as well. You look, and I say this from my angle of love, like hamster turds up there. You're bobbing all over the place.

Your facials are a mess. And frankly, with the exception of Kennedy, your tumbling wouldn't pass muster in a community center class for retired geriatric gymnasts.

(He walks to the line and gently takes CHRISSY by the hand, draws her out of the line and places his hands on her shoulders.)

Chrissy. Chrissy, Chrissy, Chrissy.

CHRISSY: Yes Coach Jay?

COACH JAY: Have you ever watched a cheer bow being made, Chrissy? I have. I spent six months apprenticed with master bow-designer Mary Louise Fernquist in her penthouse studio in Manhattan's Garment District. Each bow in her factory is lovingly hand stitched by former medalists, fluffed, sprayed with her secret-formula glitter starch, and then vacuum sealed to prevent dust from lodging in its crevasses during shipping.

CHRISSY: Wow.

COACH JAY: If Mary Louise could see your bow right now, I have no doubt that this sweet old octogenarian would set fire to her inventory and jump out the window to her own death.

CHRISSY: *(Confused:)* Is it crooked?

COACH JAY: Oh Chrissy, you poor, sweet girl. You disgust me so.

(Gently returns her to the line.)

COACH KAY: Ladies, if you're confused about what competitive cheerleading is, I suggest you take a look at Kennedy Campbell here.

(She pulls KENNEDY in front of the group.)

She's your captain for a reason. Her motions are sharp, her tumbling is clean, and if she throws it, she can damn well stick it. Kennedy, you don't have to tumble for the rest of the night. But everyone else will be doing ROTATION DRILLS for the next three hours, and all of you are going to go FULL-OUT.

(The girls groan. Coach Jay exits.)

KENNEDY: I don't mind going full out.

COACH KAY: *(Nonplussed:)* Then why don't you take an extra water break? The rest of you — get to work!

(They break into small groups and start to work out and do drills around the stage. Coach Kay pulls Kennedy aside.)

I mean it, Kennedy. You're taking it to the next level out there.

KENNEDY: Thanks, Coach!

COACH KAY: Keep it up, and you'll be first in line for that University of Louisville scholarship come spring. A little bird told me the Louisville scouts will be at Nationals this year, and their eyes are going to be on you. Now get back out there and show those other girls how to throw a pass.

(Coach Jay enters with June in tow. As they walk to center stage, the girls stop what they're doing and stare. They whisper and nudge each other. June stands awkwardly in front of them.)

GABI: Whoa, time warp.

SAM: What is *she* doing here?

KENNEDY: Is it Take Your Loser to Work Day already?

COACH JAY: Gather round, girls, we have an announcement! For those of you who don't know her already, this is June Davis. She cheered with ACD for —

COACH KAY: — seven —

COACH JAY: — seven years.

COACH KAY: Our best tumbler.

KENNEDY: More like our best *buster*.

(Gabi hushes Kennedy.)

COACH JAY: June took a little break from competitive cheerleading for a few years to find her own path. Now she's rejoined ours. She will be replacing Parker.

(The gym erupts into surprised exclamations of "What?" and "Seriously?" and "Oh, great.")

COACH KAY: *(Claps her hands loudly.)* LADIES!!

COACH JAY: And Tyler! *(Beat.)* June will need your patience and support to find her inner angle of strength again. Someday you will thank her for presenting you with the unique challenge of helping her shoulder some of her own personal burdens and failures.

CHRISSY: Thank you, June!

COACH JAY: Never ever speak, Chrissy.

COACH KAY: June's going to work hard and she's going to earn her place at Austin Cheer Depot. And if she's half as good as she used to be, she'll be better than you losers in a month. Pull it together, show her the ropes, and let's get that routine in shape for Nationals, so we can get that Worlds bid.

(Coach Kay exits.)

COACH JAY: Gabi, please help June get warmed up for jumps and make sure she knows where everything is. *(To June:)* You'll find that while some things around here are the same, others are different.

JUNE: Thank y —

COACH JAY: Namaste.

(Coach Jay exits. Awkward silence.)

JUNE: Um, hey guys. Hey, Chrissy.

CHRISSY: Hey June! I can't believe you're back! Guys, can you believe June's back?

SAM: Pretty unbelievable.

GABI: Where've you been, June?

CHRISSY: *(Quickly, in one breath:)* Yeah, what've you been up to? Were you doing high school cheerleading? I bet she was doing high school cheerleading. Were you dating a football player?

JUNE: No, I wasn't —

CHRISSY: Oh, what kind of cheer did you do? I didn't know there was any cheer besides high school cheerleading and All-Star cheerleading. Was it like with your church? What church do you go to?

JUNE: I don't go to church.

CHRISSY: That's okay, neither does Kennedy because being Catholic takes too much time away from cheer. I'm Unitarian Universalist in case you forgot, and Sam's an atheist and Gabi's Baha'i, I think that's from Jamaica or something? So where do you cheer?

JUNE: I don't. I haven't cheered since ACD.

CHRISSY: Wow, two years with no cheering at all?

GABI: So what *were* you doing, June?

CHRISSY: Yeah, June, what *were* you doing?

(Kennedy walks over and pushes past the other girls.)

KENNEDY: You guys, who cares what she was doing?

JUNE: Kennedy! Hi! It's been so long!

KENNEDY: Besides, I can answer that question for you.

JUNE: Uh, hello?

KENNEDY: *Losing*. She's been losing. Just like she lost us Worlds two years ago.

JUNE: I didn't lose you Worlds.

KENNEDY: Oh yeah? What do you call quitting the week before?

JUNE: And for your information, I win track meets all the time.

KENNEDY: Oh cool, track! Maybe she just lost it, period.

CHRISSY: Coach Jay says she took a break, Kennedy.

KENNEDY: Please, Chrissy. That's what they told us about Parker too.

JUNE: Parker Thompson? What happened?

CHRISSY: You didn't hear?

KENNEDY: Couldn't take the pressure, I guess. She was dropping Lexi all over the place for weeks before she finally took a knee in the face at Regionals. Broke her nose and got fourteen stitches *right* under her eye—a different angle and it could've popped clean out. After that she was never quite the same—couldn't even land a standing back. They say her mom had to hire a shrink to come in the car with her to practice—or she wouldn't go.

JUNE: Oh, please.

GABI: That part is true. McKenna saw the shrink, like, staring into her eyes and chanting one time.

SAM: I still think it was a hypnotist. She was totally zombie-fied at practice.

KENNEDY: One day her mom dropped her off but Parker didn't show up on the mat. Coach Kay found her under a bench in the lobby.

CHRISSY: They say she had been, like, staring at her bow for hours, not saying a word.

KENNEDY: She's probably in a psych ward somewhere now.

GABI: Actually I think she's visiting her aunt in Connecticut.

KENNEDY: Ugh! *(Annoyed:)* Whatever. The point is, some girls just can't cut it. And sorry to say, you were one of them. And you still are. So don't go loco on us, okay? Nationals are coming up, and we really can't afford to babysit another psycho.

(Kennedy looks pointedly at Chrissy.)

JUNE: Look, I didn't even want to come here, okay? I came because I have to. Just stay out of my way and I'll stay out of yours.

KENNEDY: No problem. You'll be gone in a week anyway. Looks like track hasn't exactly kept you in shape. And as soon as Coach Kay figures that out, you can go right back to Loserville *(Beat.)* and stay there.

(Kennedy exits.)

JUNE: God, what crawled up her bloomers?

GABI: Don't worry about her.

GABI: Let's just get you warmed up before Kay comes back and starts screaming again.

CHRISSY: You remember how to warm up don't you June?

JUNE: Sure.

CHRISSY: This is going to be just like old times!

(The girls begin a training routine, doing things like jumping, splits, toe-touches, crunches, push-ups, etc, in a quick sequence. June is always lagging behind them by a few seconds and messing up the moves in different ways. [This can be set to music and used as a transition to Act I, Scene 3.])

SCENE 3

(June and James are at June's house, in her bedroom.)

JUNE: So then she's all, *"And nobody heard from her ever again!"*

JAMES: I wish this Parker chick was still around. She sounds like the best of the bunch.

JUNE: I know right? *(Sighs.)* I don't know, most of them are fine. Gabi's always been cool. Sam's kinda scary but she's alright. Chrissy's—just Chrissy.

(She laughs.)

JAMES: Kennedy sounds like your run-of-the-mill sociopath.

JUNE: Yeah. The thing is, we used to be friends. I don't know what her deal is. Anyway, that's not even the worst part.

JAMES: What's the worst part? Athlete's foot?

JUNE: James! The worst part is that she's basically right. I'm not any good anymore.

JAMES: Aw, come on, June. That's not true.

JUNE: Yes it is. All my upper body strength is gone, and my tumbling is terrible. I can't even do a decent flip-flop any more.

JAMES: Oh my god, not even a *flip-flop*?

JUNE: I'm being serious!

JAMES: Come on, Junebug, you don't care about this stuff. It's—it's cheerleading! It's dumb! Remember you told me all about those, like, huge bows they wear, and how everybody's all, "You're either on the mat or you're off!"

JUNE: Yeah, I know. But—

JAMES: But nothing. You're like — so far above that stuff. You're my *Junebug*, kiddo. You're better than that.

JUNE: Yeah, I guess. *(Changing the subject:)* Hey, uh, how's Cars Eat People going?

JAMES: Oh! Really well, for once. Well, actually pretty great.

JUNE: You guys get a new bass player?

JAMES: It was a drummer, and yeah, we did a while ago. And actually — we tried out for Battle of the Bands last week.

JUNE: Oh my god, that was last week?

(She hits him.)

You should've told me, I would've brought you Twizzlers! How did it go?

JAMES: Well — actually, we made the cut. We're playing in Battle of the Bands.

JUNE: *(Squealing:)* James, that is epic!

(She hugs him. He's a little surprised.)

When is it?

JAMES: Next Friday after the pep rally. *(Beat.)* Do you think you could maybe come?

JUNE: Oh. Oh gosh, I don't know. I have practice until 7:30 every weekday, and Coach Kay is making me stay an hour late until I can land my back handsprings.

JAMES: Oh. No problem.

JUNE: But I really want to go!

JAMES: No dude, don't sweat it. It's cool.

(Pause.)

JUNE: Screw it, I'll skip out early next Friday.

JAMES: For real?

JUNE: Yeah! It's mostly conditioning on Fridays, maybe nobody'll notice. Besides, what are they gonna do, take away my birthday?

JAMES: Junebug, you're the best! If you need me to, I can come get you from practice during the pep rally.

JUNE: Great! And then I'll get to see my little Jamesy-wamesy play his wittle guitar!

(Pinches his cheek.)

JAMES: Cut it out!

(Play-slaps her hand away.)

JUNE: You cut it out!

(Slaps him back.)

JAMES: Maybe you can bring your pom-poms and cheer me on!

JUNE: We don't have pom-poms dummy.

JAMES: *(In a high-pitched voice, doing a little cheerleader dance:)* J-A-M-E-S you're the one we love the best! Go James!

JUNE: Not like that!

JAMES: Oh yeah? What's it like? Show me, oh cheery one.

JUNE: One, two, three, four!

(June starts cheering with over-the-top and purposefully silly mock enthusiasm.)

A-C-D, THE RED, BLUE, AND WHITE! THE PRIDE, OF TEXAS, THAT'S RIGHT!

JAMES: It's working already, June! I'm already a better guitar player. I think I've mastered a new chord just now watching you!

JUNE: What-EVER!

(June, really into it now, does a fake jump toward James and almost lands on him. They both fall back into the beanbag chair, laughing hysterically. Laughing:)

See what I mean? I'm terrible!

JAMES: *(Laughing:)* Oh my god, you really are! You *suck* [*stink*]!

(They laugh themselves out, and June, exhausted, flops her head over onto James's shoulder. They both sigh and settle in for a second.)

After the Battle of the Bands, maybe we could get some dinner and see a movie or something.

JUNE: You could come over and watch Space Jam, since I *know* you still haven't watched it. We can make ice cream sandwiches out of Pop Tarts, we haven't done that in forever.

JAMES: Um, really? I was sort of thinking we could go somewhere that's — not your house.

JUNE: Oh, don't worry about my parents. Now that I'm in cheer jail it's way easier to get around them. I'll just tell them —

JAMES: No, I mean — do you want to go out with me?

(June sits up straight and looks at him for the first time. He holds her gaze. She gets up abruptly and moves away.)

JUNE: Um — I think I have to be home for dinner on Friday.

JAMES: Oh! You do?

JUNE: Yeah.

JAMES: I didn't mean —

JUNE: Oh, I know! I mean, I just have to be home because my mom is like, Friday night is family night or something. I know, it's really dumb.

JAMES: I wasn't, like, asking you —

JUNE: Well, duh. I just, it's like, dinner and a movie, right?

JAMES: No! No-no-no. I meant, out with the guys. Like, Eric and Dillon and me and the new drummer guy were gonna go get something to eat and I thought maybe you'd want to hang out with us.

JUNE: Oh!

JAMES: Yeah.

JUNE: Oh.

JAMES: Yeah. Sometimes we all — like, get a little high and go to a midnight show? It's hilarious...

JUNE: Right.

JAMES: Yeah, I know you don't like that stuff so I never really ask you, but I thought, I don't know, maybe this time you would. Sorry, I know you don't like that stuff.

JUNE: Yeah, I don't.

JAMES: Okay, well...Actually, I have band practice today, so I'd better go.

JUNE: Yeah, I have to go too, gotta get to the gym.

JAMES: On Saturday?

JUNE: On every day.

JAMES: Hey — I'm going to watch Space Jam tonight. I promise.

JUNE: You better!

JAMES: I will! I'll live-Tweet it so you know I'm not lying.

JUNE: You don't even have a Twitter account!

JAMES: I'll buy one! Anything for you, Junebug.

JUNE: Hah! Chat me up instead. I'll be sitting in front of my computer all night, trying to finish my history paper with icepacks tied around my knees and ankles.

JAMES: Cool...

(An awkward pause between them.)

See you, June.

JUNE: Later, James.

SCENE 4

(In the gym. The cheerleaders drill some moves — jumps or formations, something not too distracting, toward the back of the stage. June engages in more training — she does push-ups or sit-ups [or something more difficult if the option is available]. She does as many as she can, tries really hard to do a few more, and finally just collapses.)

KENNEDY: *(Clapping:)* Nice work, June! Keep it up. God, I'm sooo glad you're on the team. You're just what we need to really sink to a new low!

JUNE: Shut up, Kennedy.

KENNEDY: No, you shut up! I had to work so hard to get this team ready for regionals, and then you come along and ruin it for everyone. God, Parker was better than you when she was catatonic.

JUNE: God, why is she always such a bitch [jerk]?

SAM: She cares too much.

JUNE: Okay.

SAM: Look, I remember how good you were before. Best Cheerleader, stunts off the chain, yada yada yada. I get it. Here's a little secret.

JUNE: *(Unimpressed:)* What?

SAM: I could be doing all that.

JUNE: Sure, whatever.

SAM: No, I really could. My sisters were. I could be too, if I tried. I just...don't. *(Shrugs.)* I don't really care about ACD, but it keeps me out of Catholic school and it keeps my parents off my back. I put in my time here, I get to keep my own hours the rest of the time. It's really not so bad if you look at it that way. I don't even have a curfew.

JUNE: Woah, really? So...what are you suggesting?

SAM: Do the bare minimum. You're good enough that you won't have to do any more than that. I'll help you out, show you a few tricks.

JUNE: You'd do that?

SAM: Sure. And don't worry about Kennedy. Ten to one she's just worried you'll steal her spot in the tumble box. As long as you don't block her shine or screw up the team, you'll get by.

(Enter Coach Jay and Coach Kay. Coach Kay claps her hands and blows her whistle.)

COACH KAY: LADIES!! Get over here NOW!!

(Everyone stops and gathers around. Coach Kay gestures toward Coach Jay.)

COACH JAY: A cheerleader is like a reed. Weave it together with other reeds, and it makes a strong, sturdy basket. Alone, it is useless—unless you bore a series of holes of varying diameters into its side, add a reed tongue, a tuning wire, and something called a shallot, and then you can play beautiful music on it.

COACH KAY: I think we all know what Coach Jay means.

(The cheerleaders shake their heads, still confused.)

What he means is Nationals are six weeks away and you ladies still look like a bunch of weak links out there on the mat. Today we're giving individual feedback. Line up at the back of the mat and wait for your name to be called.

(The girls line up in a horizontal line upstage. Coach Jay and Coach Kay go to opposite sides of downstage, to their respective

"offices." As they call each person's name, he or she runs down to stand or sit opposite them to hear feedback. When there is other dialogue happening, they are in darkness or a soft freeze. After each teammate is dismissed, he or she exits the stage.)

COACH JAY: McKenna!

COACH KAY: Genevieve!

COACH JAY: Oh McKenna, where to begin?

COACH KAY: Genevieve, I want you to look at me when I'm talking to you!

(James enters.)

JUNE: James! What are you doing here?

JAMES: I've texted you like ten times since Saturday. What's the deal?

JUNE: I've been at the gym every day.

JAMES: I watched *Space Jam*. And let me tell you, my commentary was priceless. Comic gold. I tried to chat with you the other night, you never opened your window.

JUNE: Oh yeah, I came home from the gym and just crashed really early that night. Like, I fell asleep in my workout clothes and everything.

JAMES: That's gross!

COACH KAY: Genevieve, I want you to think very, very hard about why you are here. And by that I don't mean in some kind of global, cosmic Coach Jay sense. I mean, why are you here, in my gym, on my mat, sharing *my air*? Think about it! DISMISSED!

COACH JAY: McKenna, your problem is that you think too much. I didn't get to where I am by thinking one second of any day, ever. Alright? If you're listening to *(Points to head:)* this, you're not listening to *(Points to heart:)* this, or *(Points to arm:)* this or...or...just...*(Gestures to entire body:)* the whole thing. *(Gestures to body:)* This is what is out there on the mat, not *(Gestures to head:)* this. Do you understand? Do you abuse drugs? I mean, metaphorically? I mean, don't do drugs, obviously, ever. But do drugs. Okay? Turn those brain cells off!

COACH KAY: Cassidy Clay!

COACH JAY: Cassidy Seymour!

(The two CASSIDYs are the youngest members of the cheer team, around 12-14 years old.)

JUNE: James, you have to go. You're going to get me in so much trouble.

JAMES: Hey, look at all the spandex!

JUNE: James!

JAMES: Don't you even remember why I'm here?

JUNE: What? Why?

JAMES: It's Friday! Battle of the Bands day?

(He pulls a crumpled flyer out of his pocket and hands it to her.)

COACH JAY: Cassidy Seymour, you have all the essential qualities of a top rank cheerleader, you're agile, you're strong, you have in your eyes the thirst for the blood of other girls. But I wonder about your focus. What are you thinking about right now?

CASSIDY SEYMOUR: Uh...leaving?

COACH JAY: Fair enough. Dismissed.

COACH KAY: Cassidy Clay, I feel you have been coasting by on your looks, charm, personality, talent, and…it's unacceptable. Everybody knows you do a good bow and arrow, that you look good up there. But you know what I see when I look into those eyes? My little pony, I think? I see toys in there, Clay! Toys! I want this gym to be your only toy. I want you to go home at night, and look into the mirror and say "perfection, perfection, perfection," until your jaw aches. DISMISSED!

COACH JAY: Fiona!

COACH KAY: Kendra!

JAMES: I'm here to get you out! Come on, the pep rally will be over in half an hour!

JUNE: Oh my god it's Friday already?

JAMES: Yeah. Hence all the messages?

JUNE: James I can't leave until my name is called! They're doing individual feedback. They'll know I'm gone!

JAMES: Okay, so when does your name get called?

JUNE: I don't know, I have no idea what order they're going in.

JAMES: I'll wait. Maybe you'll be next.

COACH KAY: Kendra, I look at you and I see one leg longer than the other, one arm shorter than the other, one ear larger than the other, one eye squinting a little bit. I don't know WHAT is going on with you! I want you to go home and stretch like this *(Does ridiculous stretch.)* and I want you to sleep with one knee up, like this. And if I don't see some improvement in your symmetry you're going to the back of the line! Understood? DISMISSED!

COACH JAY: Fiona, do you listen to jazz? No? That's what I thought. You're like a metronome out there. Click click click click click click click. It doesn't mean a thing if it has not got that swing. I'm bringing in 57 classic jazz albums and you're going to listen to them by the end of the week. Dismissed!

COACH KAY: Lexi!

COACH JAY: Tyler!

JUNE: *Please* go somewhere where they can't see you. If they see you I—there's no way I'll get to go.

JAMES: Okay, I'll wait over there by those giant trophies. Are any of those yours?

JUNE: *Go!*

JAMES: I'm going! Keep an eye on the time though.

(*James saunters offstage.*)

SAM: Nice one, June.

JUNE: What?

SAM: You got your boyfriend to come sneak you out of your extra practice?

JUNE: He's not my boyfriend.

SAM: Uh-huh.

GABI: He's really cute!

JUNE: James? Hardly.

GABI: Um, *yeah.* I mean, in that, like, Seth Green kind of way.

CHRISSY: Oh my god, and you are *such* a Willow!

COACH JAY: Tyler, it's just you and me, man...in an ocean of moon energy. Bro dawgs stick together, right? Ooow ow! Obviously you're doing great. Dismissed!

COACH KAY: Lexi, every time you land a standing back this pinkie moves. Did you know that? I can see the fear in you, right now, when you're doing that move. You have the fear deep in you. I want you to go home and BE FEARLESS and I don't want to see you again until that pinkie is straight in the air! Dismissed!

COACH JAY: Chrissy!

COACH KAY: Gabi!

JUNE: No really, I swear he's not my boyfriend.

SAM: Hey, I'm not judging. He's not your boyfriend, you just use him to get out of cheer practice. I get it!

(James enters and June quickly goes over to talk to him away from the other girls.)

JAMES: June! I gotta get back to school. Come on, the pep rally's almost over and I have to get there early to set up!

JUNE: I can't! If they find out I cut they'll call my parents...When do you guys play?

JAMES: We're second to last, but there's only one other band.

JUNE: What? That means you're first! Anyway...Sam has a car, as soon as we're both done I'll get a ride from her. She cuts all the time and gets away with it.

JAMES: You'll be there?

JUNE: I promise I'll be there, James.

JAMES: Okay. I'll see you there. Wish me luck, June.

JUNE: I'll do it in person.

(They quickly hug. James exits. The next set of lines are grouped to show the way the conversation alternates back and forth from one side of the stage to the other.)

COACH KAY: Gabi, you have always struck me as one of the happiest and most balanced members of our little gym community.

GABI: Awesome!

COACH KAY: Yeah, that's not a compliment. When I see that bright smile on the mat, it's great for competitions...but I can tell that it's a *real* smile, and that's not good training in my gym. I want you to do so many push-ups that you're crying on the inside while maintaining that smile on the outside. Understood? DISMISSED! Sam!

COACH JAY: Chrissy, when I'm at my lowest I look in the mirror, and do you know what I see?

CHRISSY: *(Nervously:)* No sir!

COACH JAY: You. *(Beat.)* A dark reflection of my soul, my doppelganger, that element within me manifested in the world that I must destroy or be destroyed by.

CHRISSY: Oh!

COACH JAY: But be assured, Chrissy, that I intend to destroy you...by making you a first-rate cheerleader, and leaving nothing of this *(Gesturing to her:)* behind.

CHRISSY: *(Confused and slightly worried, but still enthusiastic:)* Thank you Coach Jay!

COACH JAY: Are you with me?

CHRISSY: Okay...?

COACH JAY: Dismissed.

COACH KAY: *(Resigned:)* Sam, spit out your gum and tell your mom I said 'hello' and I'll see her at the fundraiser. DISMISSED!

COACH JAY: June!

COACH KAY: Kennedy!

(June drops the Battle of the Bands flyer on the ground before entering Jay's office.)

COACH JAY: June, we're so glad you're here.

JUNE: Really?

COACH KAY: You know, Kennedy, you remind me a lot of me when I was your age.

KENNEDY: Really?

COACH KAY: Yup. I didn't get anything handed to me either. I worked ten times as hard as everybody else and I cared ten times as much. I had the talent to back it up, and you have it too.

KENNEDY: I—I really try, Coach.

COACH JAY: June, you have taught us so much in the brief time you've been here.

JUNE: I—I have?

COACH JAY: Absolutely. You know, there was always something very...trapezoidal about you.

JUNE: Oh. Is that good?

COACH JAY: No.

COACH KAY: There's one big difference between me and you though. I captained a winning team. You're captaining a bunch of losers.

KENNEDY: We placed at Worlds last year!

COACH KAY: *(Stands.)* Sure, last year you had Kylie and Padma and Parker. Kennedy, a good captain doesn't rely on her best girls to carry the team. Think back to when you first came here. What's the first thing we learn?

KENNEDY: *(Lowers head, reciting:)* "We can't all be last pass." But I am!

COACH JAY: June, honey, I know being near the back is frustrating for you.

JUNE: Not really.

COACH JAY: Don't go pulling my leg, young lady. You weren't just any tumbler — were our *best*.

COACH KAY: Every girl wants to throw the last pass in the tumble box. It means you're at the top of your game, you're solid gold out there. The audience might only see the flyers doing the basket-toss, but the scouts in the audience know that last in the tumble box means star of the show. So, Kennedy. Who's the most important member of the team?

KENNEDY: Uh, last in the tumble box?

COACH KAY: NO! It's whoever makes them feel like a team, that's who. Those girls are a mess out there because they don't feel like a team. And that's on you.

KENNEDY: Me?

COACH JAY: You like to be the best, don't you?

JUNE: Not anymore, Coach. I just don't want to let down the team.

COACH JAY: Well, that's fortunate, because you aren't the best anymore, June. That ship has sailed.

KENNEDY: It's not my fault! Look at what I have to work with! Even Sam is doing worse this year! I mean look at June! She can barely tumble anymore!

COACH KAY: You're damn right June can't tumble. You should be working twice as hard with her, kicking her butt, getting her up to speed.

JUNE: I—I know that. I know. But I'm trying. Really, I am.

COACH JAY: And yet, you don't seem to be finding your angle of personal power, June. Right now, I'm seeing 180 degrees. Do you know what that is June?

JUNE: Um.

COACH JAY: It's not an angle, honey. It's a line.

KENNEDY: I—I'm sorry Coach.

COACH KAY: Don't be sorry, Kennedy. Fix it!

COACH JAY: I'm disappointed in you, June. Time to shape up and prove that we weren't mistaken about you.

COACH KAY: Don't let me down.

(Coach Kay and Coach Jay exit, leaving Kennedy and June alone on stage.)

SCENE 5

(June walks offstage to grab her backpack. Kennedy takes out a personal digital recorder from her bag and starts to record a voice note.)

KENNEDY: Note #84: Coach Kay just chewed me out. She said that it is my responsibility to make sure that little Junebug can do her tumbling...and if she can't, then it's all MY fault...

(June walks back in with her backpack and startles Kennedy, who rapidly puts away her voice recorder.)

(Kennedy and June are left alone on the gym mat, center stage. June takes off her cheer shoes on the edge of the mat and Kennedy stretches/shows off. Both are obviously frustrated.)

Let me guess. Unfocused? Wasting everyone's time? *(Mocking Coach Jay:)* Are you visualizing your success pyramid, Junebug?

JUNE: Don't call me that.

KENNEDY: Oh, no! I hurt the ice queen's feelings!

JUNE: I'm not an ice queen! I'm here to do my job and get out.

KENNEDY: Really? And you think you can help our team win with that loser attitude? I know your parents paid extra for the coaches to accept you back.

JUNE: What?

KENNEDY: Is that news to you?

JUNE: Leave me alone.

KENNEDY: I wish I had never met you.

(June's barely-contained calm is broken.)

JUNE: How can you say that?! Why are you being like this??

KENNEDY: I shared *everything* with you. We won duets together, like, four years in a row! You think you're above it all now.

JUNE: I...I don't. It's nothing personal. I'm sorry if I made you think it was.

KENNEDY: Nothing personal? We grew up together here! We slept at each other's houses every single weekend. I can't believe I let you into my *home*.

JUNE: Seriously? We were kids! And I don't care if you're poor Kennedy, if you live in a mobile home, or if you've always been here on scholarship. I don't go around spilling your secrets. I'm trying to stay out of your way, I know you hate me.

KENNEDY: How is it that the team's "best cheerleader" abandons everyone right before Worlds?

JUNE: I'm sure you were all too ready to take my spot in the tumble box.

KENNEDY: Well it's a good thing I was ready, wasn't it? I picked up after you once, don't think for one minute I'm in the mood to do it again. You're either on the mat or you're off.

JUNE: Oh my *god*, are you still saying that? Even the six-year-olds think that's dumb.

KENNEDY: Whatever. I'm sure you love it, standing in the back and mocking us all. It's pathetic.

(Chrissy, Sam, and Gabi slowly appear near the back of the gym; they've come back to retrieve something and have caught the argument.)

JUNE: You have no idea how I feel.

KENNEDY: I don't care about your mushy disgusting feelings! I care about this team. I don't know why you had to come back here, of all places. I'm sure the "cheer bears" at Cheer Euphoria in Pflugerville would have loved to have you. You could have helped them land their cartwheels and won a shiny participant ribbon. This is my last year at ACD and YOU. ARE. RUINING. IT.

JUNE: Well, I'm sorry! I can't quit this time! *(Beat.)* I'm not trying to bring the team down. I'm here, aren't I? I'm working on it! Why is every fucking [single] person in my life trying to smack me in the face. I get it! I hear you! I SUCK!

KENNEDY: You deserve worse. You have everything you could ever want right in front of you and you're too self-pitying to do anything with it. Aw, you look like you're about to cry, Junie.

GABI: *(Loudly:)* I could have sworn I left my backpack somewhere over here...

CHRISSY: Oh my gosh, June and Kennedy! I didn't know you two were still here! We just walked in, right now and we didn't overhear — OW!

(Sam elbows Chrissy.)

SAM: Hey June, is Gabi's backpack over there?

(June sees it on the floor by the mat.)

JUNE: Yeah, it's over here.

KENNEDY: And here I was daydreaming that you three came back to put in some extra practice time. Silly me.

(Gabi, Chrissy, and Sam make their way toward June and Kennedy.)

GABI: It's Friday.

CHRISSY: We're all going to Rumba Punch for Smoothie Smappy Hour and everyone is invited!

SAM: June, you should come with us.

CHRISSY: Yes yes yes! June, you have to! I have so much I want to ask you! I don't even know what your favorite color is now! It was pink when we first met but then later you said you liked purple better and now I have NO IDEA!

JUNE: Hmm. I don't know. I feel sick. I can't...think right now.

SAM: Well, then you definitely shouldn't stay late. Hey, no worries. I'll call your dad and tell him you're with us. Your parents love me.

JUNE: True. *(Smiling slightly:)* Okay. Sure. *(Taking a look at Kennedy:)* Let's get out of here.

KENNEDY: Cutting out early? Predictable. Pathetic.

(As Kennedy and June shoot eye-daggers at each other before the other three girls come in to whisk June away with them. Kennedy is left alone and sees the flyer for the BATTLE OF THE BANDS sitting on the ground. She picks it up, reads it, and walks offstage with it in hand.)

SCENE 6

(At the local Rumba Punch cafe, a cheery and upbeat place. Colorful chairs sit around a small table where Gabi, Chrissy, and Sam are seated around June. They all drink from the smoothie cups while Muzac plays softly in the background.)

CHRISSY: This is perfect! All of us hanging out. I feel like a real teenager!

SAM: Chrissy, you are a real teenager. You've been one for several years now.

CHRISSY: Aw, thanks Sam!

GABI: Don't worry about it, June, I think we all got reamed by the coaches.

JUNE: Yeah. Well, I bet Kennedy wasn't.

SAM: You kidding? I know she was. That's why she was so keyed up back there. Anyway, you should just ignore her. She's been acting like that for a while.

GABI: Angry Cheer Bot 3000 ever since she became captain.

CHRISSY: I'm sure she didn't mean it, June! She tells me all the time that I shouldn't be at ACD—but I'm still here! I just visualize everyone smiling whenever they yell at me and it works really well!

SAM: Now that the Louisville scholarship is in her sights, she's probably stopped sleeping and subsists only on power bars and fear.

JUNE: There's a scholarship?

GABI: Ever since ACD was featured on—

GABI, SAM, CHRISSY: ESPN 7's Top 10 Best Cheer Gyms in the Greater Southwest!

GABI: —a scout has come from Louisville every year to hand pick one senior girl to offer a full freakin' ride.

JUNE: Kennedy is a shoe-in for that. A full ride? I bet she wants it more than anything.

CHRISSY: She has a Pinterest board devoted to Louisville! I saw it! I follow that board. Oops, does this count as gossip? I like Kennedy. I don't want to gossip about her.

SAM: This is what being a real teenager is like, Chrissy.

CHRISSY: (*Conflicted:*) Oh...

GABI: So, speaking of gossip...Bryan asked me if I wanted to visit his parents in Colorado at their ski resort.

CHRISSY: Oh my gosh! Your life is like a movie! Are you gonna go!?

GABI: Nah. I have to plan my school's honors society banquet and study for AP exams. Plus, I think I'm going to dump him soon.

JUNE: Is this guy in college?

GABI: No, he's 28.

JUNE: Woah.

SAM: Gabi met him at the 360 overlook. He runs some tech start-up downtown.

GABI: He's nice but I don't think we're that compatible.

JUNE: I can't believe your mom lets you date...older guys like that.

GABI: She's cool. She trusts my judgment.

CHRISSY: Do you have a boyfriend, June? You're really pretty! I bet you dated lots of cool guys when you were away.

JUNE: Oh my god JAMES. Oh my god I can't believe I—ahhhhh!

CHRISSY: What is it?

SAM: Forget your anniversary or something?

JUNE: He is NOT my boyfriend already, and no, I forgot something way, way worse. I am so stupid, how could I be so stupid? *(Grabbing her stuff:)* I gotta go, guys. Thanks. I mean, really—thanks, you're the first girls to actually be nice to me at ACD since I've been back. I thought I didn't have friends there any more.

GABI: We're totally your friends.

CHRISSY: Let's have a sleepover!

SAM: Um, no to sleepover. But yes to friends.

JUNE: Thanks guys. I'll see you later.

(June runs out of the Rumba Punch, cellphone in hand, texting like mad.)

SCENE 7

(The gym. June and Gabi help base a simple stunt in the gym, or have just finished something. Kennedy oversees the stunt and seems slightly more cheerful than usual.)

KENNEDY: Wow. That didn't suck. Take five and then we'll try the whole sequence!

(June and Gabi walk off to the side together to grab a drink of water.)

JUNE: Oh my God, did I just hear Kennedy give us...a tiny crumb of praise?

GABI: You heard it too? I was beginning to think I was having a hallucination.

JUNE: I think the team is getting...tighter.

GABI: That, or Kennedy is getting looser.

JUNE: Impossible!

GABI: Maaaaybe she's back on anti-anxiety medication...or she got laid.

JUNE: *(Shushing her:)* Shhhh! Whatever! Kennedy has never had a boyfriend. They're against her rules.

GABI: Speaking of boyfriends...

(James has walked into the gym and awkwardly shuffles around, looking at the floor.)

JUNE: Oh my God! Finally!

(She rushes over to him.)

James! I've been trying to call you! I must have texted you 100 times! I'm so, so, so sorry I—

JAMES: *(Interrupting:)* Save it. If I wanted to hear it, I would have answered one of your calls.

JUNE: But you don't understand, I was just having the absolute worst day and I couldn't catch a break.

JAMES: Because you stayed late at the gym?

JUNE: Well, I...I went to the school. I did! I just got there too late.

JAMES: How was smoothie smappy hour?

JUNE: How did you know about...?

JAMES: Look! It's not important. I told myself I wouldn't get into it, that I wouldn't talk to you about it...but here I am.

JUNE: James, please, please don't stay angry at me. I really need you right now and —

JAMES: No, dude! *I* needed *you!* This was the one time I've asked you for anything. You promised me. You looked me right in the eye and you promised me. I spent the whole damn set looking for you in the audience. I couldn't concentrate. We lost to that idiot Mr. ComputerHands the iPad DJ. We had a whole band and he had one freaking tablet and WE LOST TO HIM.

JUNE: I'm so sorry, I bet you guys were awesome.

JAMES: June, I don't want to know what you think. I'm sick of wondering what you think. I've been going out of my mind this past month. You may have texted and called me a lot the past few days, but before that — radio silence.

JUNE: Dude, you know the deal! I've been here!

JAMES: Except on Friday night.

JUNE: That was the one time! I admitted that that was totally and completely my fault.

JAMES: Look, I think it's better if we don't see each other for a little while.

(June is completely stunned.)

JUNE: What...? Well, why did you come here?

JAMES: I, um, I didn't come here to see you.

(Kennedy has spied James from across the room and comes bounding over.)

KENNEDY: *(Squealing in an uncharacteristically girly way:)* James!

(Kennedy and James share a brief hug, Kennedy initiating it.)

JAMES: Hey!

KENNEDY: I got your text. My mom says I can go out after practice is over.

JUNE: What is this? April Fools?

KENNEDY: Can you butt out for a minute, June? I need to talk to my friend.

JUNE: *Your* friend? Woah. No. This is not happening.

(June drags James away from Kennedy.)

James, what the hell do you think you're doing?

JAMES: Whatever I want to do, June! You don't have exclusive friend rights over me.

JUNE: I think I can have some say over this one specific situation—she's a sociopath, remember? If this is a joke, an intervention—I get it! I've learned my lesson. Stop playing around.

JAMES: It's not a joke. Kennedy's really not that bad once you get to know her. She came to the show on Friday and we hung out afterward. Besides, I told you. I think we should take a break. You're obviously busy —

JUNE: Not. That. Bad?! Whatever! Whatever. This is ridiculous.

JAMES: You've already made your choice, June. Now let me make mine!

JUNE: FINE! Enjoy your neurotic mis-matched bliss! I've got to get back on the mat.

(June storms back to the center of the mat just as Coach Kay comes out, blowing her whistle.)

COACH KAY: Alright ladies and Tyler, now that we've got a handle on the stunts, let's practice some tumbling. Kennedy, do you want to try your tumble pass first?

JUNE: Coach, can I go?

COACH KAY: *(Surprised:)* June, I thought you didn't want to be in the tumble box.

JUNE: I want it more than anything I've ever wanted in my entire life.

COACH KAY: Sure, go for it.

(The other girls gather around and whisper to each other. June walks to the edge of the mat and prepares to tumble, arms raised. She shoots Kennedy a cocky look.)

SAM: Damn. She's back.

CHRISSY: *(In awe:)* June is *on the mat.*

(Hard blackout [and immediate music strongly suggested].)

(End of Act I. Optional Intermission.)

ACT II

SCENE 1

(Act II opens with the team 1: doing the same routine from the top of Act I, but better; or 2: doing another small segment from another part of the routine; or 3: having just finished a "routine" with the lights coming up just in time to see the final pose. The routine is well-executed, and June and Kennedy are near the front/in visible positions. June now looks like a different girl. She wears an ACD tank-top and her hair high in a clean ponytail with a bright, large bow. She smiles brightly. Kennedy, by contrast, looks harried for the first time. Her hair messily hangs out of her ponytail and she's frowning and fumbling.)

(Coach Kay and Coach Jay enter.)

COACH KAY: Ladies, this is the best job I've seen you do yet! Finally, we are sticking it! Overall, it looked good. McKenna, you were super sharp that time, and it made a huge difference. June, I know Chrissy stamped on your foot twice, but you didn't even flinch. That was a pro move. You were focused and clean. Gabi, remember your facials, if you're not smiling it's hard for the judges to notice that you're actually doing your job. Chrissy, you weren't...you know what? You stayed in rhythm and smiled. Kennedy...this is the fifth time I've had to tell you to perk up. I don't know what's going on but you look like dog meat out there. Are you sick?

KENNEDY: No ma'am. I just got confused.

COACH KAY: Confused? You should be eating, sleeping, and dreaming of this routine by now. Watch out, if you don't shape up, I'm gonna give June your last pass.

KENNEDY: What? But I—

COACH JAY: It's not your place to question us, Kennedy.

KENNEDY: Yes sir.

(Kennedy looks crestfallen and June tries to hide her glee.)

COACH JAY: Speaking of opportunities, don't forget that our big Spring "FUN"-raiser is coming up this Saturday. Chrissy McCarthy's saint-like parents have graciously booked their church parking lot for us and Rumba Punch is sponsoring concessions for the fifth year in a row.

COACH KAY: In addition to the usual—car wash, dunking booth, silent auction—all the top winners from last year's individual events will have an opportunity to perform their routines.

COACH JAY: Tell your parents, your little school friends, your youth pastors, your Myspace Top eight. Money doesn't make the world go 'round, but it does help us to book nicer accommodations and perhaps an extra day at Epcot if we make it to Worlds.

ALL CHEERLEADERS EXCEPT KENNEDY: *(Excitedly overlapping:)* Yeah, Disney!
Epcot!
Oh my god!
Yes!! *(Etc.)*

COACH KAY: Alright, settle down! Let's do some conditioning and then call it a night!

> *(June immediately drops to floor to start her side sit-ups. Gabi, Sam, and Chrissy come near her to work out. They are slower to start.)*

GABI: Man! I thought I was doing so well! Normally I feel like I can't stop smiling.

JUNE: *(Still doing sit-ups:)* You rarely smile when you're working on the routine. It's kinda a problem.

GABI: ...Yeah. I'm gonna work on it.

CHRISSY: Did you hear that Gabi? What Coach Kay said? I was in rhythm!

JUNE: See? I told you practicing the motions at home to the music would help.

CHRISSY: It really did!

JUNE: But seriously, you've got to stop stepping on my feet. If my shoelaces came untied —

SAM: *(Interrupting:)* It would be the end of the world?

JUNE: It would be *lame* and potentially dangerous.

SAM: Oh, so not so different from the rest of cheerleading.

JUNE: Whatever!

(June playfully shoves Sam.)

CHRISSY: June, you've been doing so well! I really admire you! You've worked so hard, and you're so focused!

JUNE: Thanks! Umm. Chrissy...I can't help but notice that you're not doing *any* conditioning.

CHRISSY: Oh, wow, you're right!

JUNE: Umm...I think you're just really distracted around other people. Perhaps your time would be better spent if you worked out alone over there. No offense!

CHRISSY: Oh. Okay, yeah. You're probably right. Thank you, June! See you girls later! Just let me know when you want me to come back over!

(She slowly leaves to go work out alone.)

SAM: What's up today, Cruella De Vil, you into kicking puppies now too?

JUNE: What's wrong with being blunt with Chrissy?

SAM: You know 90% of the reason she comes here is to talk about church, and look at people's faces.

JUNE: I don't think she'll keep a lot of friends if she falls over at Nationals.

GABI: Yeah, this is my last year at ACD. If we lost because of something like that...

JUNE: Yeah, it would be super lame.

SAM: Ugh!

JUNE: Where's Kennedy? She looked like she was going to throw up earlier.

GABI: Well, she doesn't look like that now.

(Kennedy and James step into view on stage left. They casually talk, but Kennedy makes a point of touching him during the conversation, and checking over her shoulder to make sure June sees every moment.)

JUNE: Ugh. Seriously?

(Coach Kay and Jay enter from stage right.)

COACH JAY: June Davis, do you have a moment?

JUNE: Yes, sir.

(She immediately gets up and makes a beeline for the coaches, practically jogging.)

COACH JAY: We don't want to get your hopes up.

COACH KAY: But it seemed like you should know where you stand.

COACH JAY: June, you've really stepped up. Your angles are strong and your power is palpable.

COACH KAY: What he means to say is, we're considering you for last in the tumble box.

JUNE: Oh my gosh, really??

COACH KAY: Show Jay that tumbling pass, would you?

JUNE: Sure!

COACH KAY: HEY YOU, LADIES, CLEAR OFF THE MAT!

(The girls on the mat scatter, making room for June. There are three options for staging this next moment: 1: June walks offstage and a doppelganger [real cheerleader/gymnast] in the exact same outfit walks on and does a tumbling pass with her face upstage, running off at the end so June can come on as if she has done the move; 2: June does a tumbling pass in front of the audience [the actor must be trained and have safe conditions for tumbling]; 3: June exits to tumble, and the onstage cast "watches" her complete her pass out of sight. As soon as she finishes, she runs back onstage. [This moment doesn't have to be perfect and was used as a joke as well as a plot device in the original production].)

See what I mean? Amazing.

COACH JAY: I almost can't believe it.

COACH KAY: If you can keep that up for the next week, you've got that spot at Nationals.

JUNE: Thank you, Coach! I won't let you down!

COACH JAY: Your cheer-future is becoming brighter every day, Miss Davis. If I had that kind of tenacity after such utter failure, I may have made it to the 1996 Olympics. But alas, back then, before PowerPPP, my mind was like a fragile sparrow in a shiny brass cage. You could put a blanket over me and I'd forget where I was.

JUNE: That sounds...rough.

COACH KAY: Keep up the good work, June, you may be doing this for a while longer.

(She gives June a knowing look. The coaches exit stage right.)

JAMES: *(Forgetting himself for a moment:)* Woah, that was pretty good! I mean...whatever.

KENNEDY: James, you promised yourself you would stop obsessing over her. It's not healthy. And besides, it wasn't *that* great.

JAMES: I'm not being obsessive, that was just really cool. Everyone else seemed impressed.

(June tentatively walks toward Kennedy and James.)

JUNE: Is it okay if I say hi?

KENNEDY: *(In a cutesy fake-nice voice:)* You actually need to stick the pass, you can't just run off at the end like you're at a track meet.

JUNE: *(Cutesy voice back:)* Okay...thanks!

JAMES: Hey.

JUNE: Hey.

KENNEDY: James and I were just leaving.

JUNE: You're not sticking around for extra practice? Weird. That's the third time this week, Kenny.

KENNEDY: Don't call me that.

JUNE: Okay, well, it's your...missed opportunity. Boy, it's gonna feel great to have that last spot in the tumble box after all this time.

(Kennedy's jaw drops open in disbelief.)

Sorry.

(June shrugs, not sorry at all.)

(Immediate cut to upbeat, preferably cocky dance music [Suggestion: "Sorry for Party Rocking" by LMFAO]. June starts dancing in a celebratory way. Kennedy angrily storms off, her recorder left on the ground near where she was standing. James trails behind her. June keeps dancing until she stumbles into the voice recorder, almost crushing it with her foot. She picks it up, slightly confused as to why it's there.)

(The music fades out.)

Who has a voice recorder?

(She presses the button and one of Kennedy's voice notes plays.)

KENNEDY (V.O.): Note #84. You're getting anxiety pimples again, Kennedy. Stop rubbing your grubby hands all over your face when you're nervous.

JUNE: *(Laughing:)* Oh my God. Kennedy records *voice notes* for herself. *(Parroting Kennedy from earlier:)* Predictable. Pathetic.

(Music starts up again and June dances off, recorder still in her hand.)

SCENE 2

(The scene is the parking lot of Chrissy's church. There's a mat center. Somewhere behind the mat there's a banner that says, "Take AUSTIN CHEER DEPOT to Nationals!" Several cheerleaders [not leads] are stretching on the mat. Downstage left is a folding table with assorted snacks laid out in rows. There is a sign on the table that says, "Austin Cheer Depot is proudly sponsored by RUMBA PUNCH." There's a folding chair behind the table, and an Igloo filled with bottled smoothies. Throughout the scene, people come up to the table and silently buy snacks from the table.)

(Coach Jay is seated downstage, staring silently at the PA system, which is hooked up to a laptop. Sam and Gabi enter, carrying buckets, sponges, and squeegees. They wear super short cut-offs and t-shirts tied up over their navels.)

SAM: Well, this is humiliating.

GABI: What, the outfits? I think they're cute. *(Craning her neck to see behind her:)* Hey cool, you can even see a little bit of my butt tattoo!

SAM: Every year at the fundraiser, it's the same thing. It's not enough that we have to do cheerleading in a public parking lot and have a dunking booth and push kale bars and Rumba Riptides on everybody. We also have to have girls in daisy dukes scrubbing windshields for lech-y old dudes. Not that I care, but it's kind of a *cliché*.

(Chrissy enters in similar outfit, so excited she can barely contain herself.)

CHRISSY: Oh my god y'all, are you talking French again? That is so classy! Let me try! *Baguette.*

SAM: Chrissy, is your church okay with their parking lot looking like a music video from the 80s?

CHRISSY: We're Unitarian Universalists!

GABI: Sam, if you didn't want to be on the car wash team, why did you sign up?

SAM: Because otherwise they were going to make me do my floor routine from Nationals last year. I'd rather swallow a rock.

CHRISSY: Gosh, I wish my floor routine had won at Nationals last year so they would ask me to do mine. Don't you, Gabi?

GABI: Naw, I like washing cars. Besides, Caleb's going to show up with his new girlfriend Becca and I want to make sure she sees what a stone fox I am.

SAM: Trying to make some poor girl jealous? That doesn't seem very girl-power of you, Gabi.

GABI: No man, Caleb instagrammed Becca and me kissing in a hot tub last night and now I'm kind of into her. Who knew?

(Gabi walks off.)

SAM: *(Turning to Chrissy:)* Huh. Learn something new everyday.

CHRISSY: I don't get it.

SAM: Nevermind. Let's go see if there's any more Fruit Roll-Ups.

CHRISSY: Yay!

(They walk off together.)

(Enter June. She walks over and studies the frustration of Coach Jay.)

JUNE: What are you doing, Coach?

COACH JAY: *(Startled:)* Ah! Oh...this PA system is...challenging me.

JUNE: Oh.

COACH JAY: At first I was trying to push *it* to perform. That was a mistake. Now I am pushing *myself* to perform.

JUNE: Huh.

COACH JAY: When we push *ourselves* to perform, we exert a *pull* on our surroundings, *re*-forming the world around us. *Per*form. *Re*form. *Per*form. *Re*form.

JUNE: Is it working?

COACH JAY: I won't know for some time.

JUNE: Do you want me to just help?

COACH JAY: That'd be great.

(Gets up quickly and walks off.)

(June leans over, finds the right cord, plugs the laptop in, shrugs, and starts to walk away. Then she thinks of something. She pulls Kennedy's recorder out of her backpack and looks at it for a second, hesitating. Then all of a sudden she bends down and plugs it into the laptop, hurriedly does a few things on the screen, unplugs the recorder and steps away. She starts to put the recorder back in her backpack, then thinks better of it and hides it up her sleeve instead. Looking nervously around for a place to drop it, she backs up, bumping right into Barbara, who has just come on stage with a money box.)

BARBARA: June-y!

JUNE: Mom! What are you doing here?

BARBARA: Did you forget? Your father and I are helping out with the fundraiser.

JUNE: You know I'm not doing a routine, right? It's all the winners from last year.

BARBARA: We know June-y. We just figure as long as you have to be out here we should be too. I'm doing concessions and your father's going to tape it for YouTube. Coach Jay thinks it could go viral.

JUNE: Well—thanks, I guess. Uh Mom, I have to go—I should be helping.

BARBARA: Hang on there, June, this will only take a second. *(Beat.)* Sweetie, I know your father and I have been a little hard on you lately.

JUNE: *(Distracted:)* It's fine, Mom. Don't worry about it.

BARBARA: This whole cheerleading thing wasn't your idea. But you have taken this whole situation and really turned it around.

JUNE: It was no big deal, really.

BARBARA: No really. Life gave you lemons and you turned them into a Lemon Blast-Off Rumba Shake.

JUNE: Yeah Mom.

BARBARA: June. We're *proud* of you.

(June snaps to attention for the first time.)

JUNE: You—you are?

BARBARA: Yes, June-y. We know how hard you've been working to catch up to those other girls. And now Coach Kay tells us you might be up for a scholarship! These past two years it seemed like you were just drifting away. We missed you so much. *(Putting her hand on June's cheek:)* And now we have you back.

JUNE: I missed you guys too.

BARBARA: We always knew there was still a winner in there somewhere!

(This hurts. June takes a step backward. Meanwhile, Bob has entered with a handheld recorder. He approaches June with the camera from behind.)

BOB: Hi honey!!

JUNE: *(Startled and jumpy:)* Ah! Dad!

BOB: Anything you want to say about the big competition coming up?

JUNE: Uh, no.

BARBARA: Nothing? Come on Junie!

JUNE: Okay, fine. *(Fake perky:)* Austin Cheer Depot is really gonna bring it this year at Nationals! Because ultimately it comes down to heart and how much you want to win! At ACD we always say — You're either on the mat or you're off! And we're totally *on!*

(June executes a fakey little cheer move.)

BOB: Okay that's great! Now Barb, come over here.

(June moves away from her parents, toward the concession table and crowds of teens upstage. Barbara crosses so that she's in front of the camera now, talking to Bob. The camera should be pointed to where it catches whatever June is doing in the background. During the next several lines, June wanders to the concession table, carefully bends down and drops the recorder on the ground underneath it, nudging it with her foot. She looks around worried, and exits stage left.)

BARBARA: *(Embarrassed but pleased:)* What should I say?

BOB: You were a cheerleader once! Tell us what it was like.

BARBARA: Well that was a different kind of cheerleading, we cheered for the football team at the high school.

BOB: I seem to remember the cheerleaders coming to basketball games, too.

BARBARA: Oh Bobby, that was way back in the dark ages.

BOB: I know there was one particular basketball player who always felt like they were cheering just for him.

BARBARA: Well maybe *one* of them was.

(Bob kisses Barbara on the cheek.)

BOB: I'd love to stay here, but I see that Coach Kay just got into the dunking booth. I'm going to go take my shot at that radioactive harridan.

BARBARA: Bob!

BOB: What? We're paying enough!

(Bob exits stage left. June nervously enters with Chrissy in tow.)

CHRISSY: Oh my gosh, don't you think this is basically the best possible way to spend a Saturday? I think overcast is better than sunny, don't you? Because it doesn't cause as much cancer. That's why I don't eat meat either. Cancer. I mean that and the animals. Some people think if you're going to kill an animal to eat it, cancer is, like, just what you deserve. But I say let God sort it out, I'm just here to cheer! *(Does a little cheer move.)*

(Kennedy enters stage left.)

KENNEDY: Keep practicing Chrissy, maybe you'll be moved to the center of the back row someday! June, I guess it would be too much to ask you to actually help.

JUNE: I don't see you blowing up any balloons.

KENNEDY: I'm helping by performing my winning routine from last year. Doesn't look like you made the cut.

CHRISSY: That's because she wasn't at Nationals last year, Kennedy. Remember? Otherwise June would totally be doing a routine!

KENNEDY: What's your excuse, Chrissy? You were at last year's Nationals. How come nobody asked you?

JUNE: Kennedy, don't be like that! Not here.

KENNEDY: I'm just saying. Winners win, and losers lose. The mat is for winners, and I don't see either of you on it.

JUNE: Shut up, Kennedy!

CHRISSY: It's okay, June. Kennedy's right, I'm not that great at cheering and every time Coach Jay looks at me he cries. I can still help the team out by washing cars, right? I'm pretty good at that.

JUNE: Chrissy, you're good at lots of things!

CHRISSY: *(Holding back tears while exiting:)* No I'm not!

(She leaves. Even Kennedy looks a little nonplussed.)

JUNE: You know what Kennedy? Someday, someone is going to get back at you for being such a miserable bitch [so horribly nasty to people]. And it may happen sooner than you think.

(Coach Kay enters with a bullhorn, toweling herself off. The two girls, who have been facing off center stage in front of the mat, back off as Kay goes to the middle.)

COACH KAY: Thanks for coming out to raise money to take our girls to Nationals! This year we're going to kick it into high gear! But first, some performances from last year's champions—to show you that ACD doesn't just go to competitions, we WIN them!!

(The cheerleaders and family members watching cheer and yell excitedly. James enters, watches from a distance.)

First up—you know her as the senior five captain, last year this routine won her Best Cheerleader at Nationals and second at Worlds: Kennedy Campbell!!

(Coach Jay clicks the mouse on the laptop. Kennedy gets up on the mat and starts her first tumble pass or stunt.)

(Suddenly the music stops and is replaced by a recording of Kennedy's voice.)

KENNEDY RECORDING: Note #86: Stop eating blueberries, Kennedy. They're making you fat, plus they're staining your teeth. Note #87: Fix your back handspring, left foot is a quarter inch too far forward on landing. Note #88: Point your right foot out more when you walk. Second toes should be parallel at all times.

(By now everybody's laughing except Kennedy, who's frozen.)

Note #90: Get money from dad to get teeth whitened again. Note #92: Stop crying in the bathroom, it makes you look weak and everybody can tell.

KENNEDY: Turn it off! Turn it off! Oh my god, no.

(Coach Jay fumbles cluelessly with the equipment. The crowd has gone silent.)

KENNEDY RECORDING: Note #93: Write down the name of Sam's makeup and tell Dad Mom can't afford it. Note #94: Get your fat ass in shape, do you want June to beat you at everything like she did last time?

(James yanks the plug on the PA, and the recording stops with a screech. Kennedy cries on the mat.)

KENNEDY: I *hate* you guys! I hate you!

JAMES: Hey Kennedy, let's go.

(He takes Kennedy's hand and pulls her off the mat. They exit together.)

COACH KAY: Jay! What the hell was that?

COACH JAY: Now don't go blaming me for something that happened on the *internet!*

(Bob runs up with the camera, followed by Barbara. All the adults argue and talk over each other very rapidly. The teens also gossip and whisper excitedly.)

BOB: Jason, Katherine, I want to reassure you that the video will not include what just happened.

COACH KAY: Oh, it better not. Please hand that tape over right now.

BARBARA: Well I want to know how something like that could have happened in your gym and you not know about it!

COACH JAY: We're not technically in the gym, we're in the Unitarian Universalist church parking lot.

BARBARA: Don't you nickel and dime me, mister! That could have been my June up there!

JUNE: Mom...

BOB: Yeah, what's going on here anyway, Jason? Who's in charge? What is this, *Carrie?*

BARBARA: What kind of mean-girl place are you running?

COACH JAY: I assure you, we will find the girl responsible and —

BOB: And what, Jay? Use a protractor to straighten her out?

COACH KAY: That is enough sir! If you want your daughter to stay in this gym, you will button it!

(Gabi has walked over with the recorder and tries to get a word in, but no one seems to hear or see her.)

GABI: Hey! Hey!

BARBARA: Maybe June would be better off at Austin Cheer Corps!

COACH KAY: Don't you mention that name in my gym!

GABI: Excuse me!

BOB: We're not in your gym, we're in the Unitarian Universalist church parking lot!

GABI: Guys!

COACH JAY: What? Gabi? What? What? What? Everyone listen to Gabi! Gabi is going to say something right now! What, Gabi? What?

GABI: Look, I found Kennedy's recorder!

SAM: She was looking for it all day yesterday.

COACH KAY: I'll take that.

(She snatches the recorder out of Gabi's hands.)

It's evidence!

(Coach Jay gently takes the recorder away from Coach Kay.)

COACH JAY: Actually we're probably just going to give it back to Kennedy.

COACH KAY: Where did you find it, GABI?

GABI: It was right over here under the concession table. What? Anyone could have dropped it there!

BARBARA: Well I've had enough. This is the worst fundraiser we've ever been to.

COACH JAY: FUN-raiser.

CHRISSY: And it's starting to rain.

COACH KAY: *(Into bullhorn:)* Folks, don't just stand around like idiots, grab the equipment!

JUNE: Can we just go home, Mom?

BARBARA: Sure, baby. Come on, let's go.

SCENE 3

(June's house, in the back yard. June practices her jumps/works out. She has obviously exhausted herself, and is frustrated with every action she makes. Barbara comes out with a telephone in one hand, covering the receiver with the other.)

BARBARA: June, it's Sam again.

JUNE: Ugh! Tell her I'm in the bathroom.

(June's out of breath but continues to push herself while talking.)

BARBARA: Again? She'll think we're poisoning you.

JUNE: Just tell her I'm not home!

BARBARA: Okay. *(Into receiver:)* I'm sorry Sam, Bob says she just ran out the door. *(Pause.)* I'm not sure when she's getting back in, but I'll let her know. *(Pushes button to hang up and sighs.)* Sweetie, Sam and the other girls are watching a movie tonight, you sure you don't want to go out with them?

JUNE: Mom, Nationals are this weekend! I need to stay here and practice until it's time for bed.

BARBARA: But sweetie, you've been working so hard. Why don't you just take a break and clear your head before the competition, like the other girls are? You're not—avoiding them, are you?

JUNE: No! Mom, my toe-touch is still low. The last thing I want is to look like an idiot at Nationals. You guys wanted me to be a winner, right?

BARBARA: *(Stung:)* Of course, June. Do whatever you need to. We'll be inside watching TV, you can join us any time.

(Barbara exits. June keeps jumping/working out, concentrating hard. James enters.)

JAMES: I can't believe you.

JUNE: James! What are you — how's it going?

JAMES: Getting in some good practice? Gonna impress those scouts and get that scholarship tomorrow? Really wipe out the competition?

JUNE: As a matter of fact, yeah. I'm gonna try. Is that a problem for you?

JAMES: I don't know, maybe it shouldn't be. Ever since you started this thing again, you've been like a totally different person. But June — I didn't think you would do something like *that*.

JUNE: Like what?

JAMES: Stealing Kennedy's recorder? So you could embarrass her in front of everyone?

JUNE: I — I didn't —

JAMES: Oh please deny it! Please do that. I can show you the proof. I have the video right here on my phone.

JUNE: What video?

JAMES: The video your dad posted online of the fundraiser.

(James pulls out his smart phone and shows June the screen.)

JUNE: Oh my god...

JAMES: Yeah. Blink and you could miss it. Maybe if I didn't always know exactly where you were in every frame of every one of these stupid videos... *(Brushing a sleeve across his eyes angrily:)* But there you are in the background, hiding something under the table, right where Gabi found Kennedy's recorder. You've finished up your little plot and now you're getting rid of the evidence.

JUNE: James, it wasn't like that!

JAMES: What was it like?

JUNE: *(Approaching tears:)* I found it on the floor, and I had to listen to find out whose it was, and then I—I thought it would be funny. I thought it would, you know, take her down a notch. But I didn't think it would be like that! I swear I wouldn't have done it if I had known everything that was on that tape. It's just, she was being so rude to everyone, even Chrissy! I—

JAMES: You just decided to publicly humiliate her.

JUNE: *(Really angry now:)* Kennedy has been nothing but mean to me from day one! I know she's your *girlfriend* and all—

JAMES: She's not my girlfriend! We're just friends!

JUNE: —but you don't see her when she's making my life a living hell!! But I guess she matters more to you than my feelings.

JAMES: Oh don't start that. You don't want to start that.

JUNE: Start what?

JAMES: I think we both know whose feelings matter around here, and they're not mine! They never were!

JUNE: I have always been there for you!

JAMES: Just like you were there for me the one night it actually mattered.

JUNE: Well I'm sorry you didn't win.

JAMES: I didn't care that much about winning, June! It's about being there for your friends. You used me, June-y. How I know you used me, is you went away the minute I asked you for anything at all.

JUNE: I — I wasn't ready, James! You took me by surprise!

JAMES: How? We hung out and stared at each other every day for like ten years. Nothing you could say or do would ever surprise me, how could I possibly take you by surprise?

JUNE: But that's just it. All this time I thought we were friends because — I'm cool, and you're cool, because we're cool when we're together —

JAMES: Exactly!

JUNE: — and then it turns out there was this other thing you wanted from me, and I didn't even know. *(Beat.)* How long — when did you start feeling that way?

JAMES: I don't know, June. It's not something I knew was gonna happen! It just started happening, and I don't know, I didn't want to tell you, because —

JUNE: — because it might freak me out.

JAMES: Yeah, clearly. June, I'm the only guy at school who's best friends with a girl. The guys have been teasing me about you since freshman year, and I always said, hey man, she's just a really cool person who's super fun to hang out with and who gets everything about me and I get everything about her too.

JUNE: James, I —

JAMES: Except I don't. I thought I did, but I don't. Because the June I knew would never do something that mean and horrible and petty to another person. Just because she was afraid.

JUNE: Afraid?

JAMES: Yeah, June. You've always been afraid.

JUNE: Of what?

JAMES: Of not being the *best*.

JUNE: *(Trying to shrug his words off:)* That's ridiculous. I don't care about that stuff.

JAMES: Yeah, sure. That's why you dropped out of cheerleading, right? Kennedy says you quit because you—busted a move, or something.

JUNE: *(Understanding:)* Oh. Yeah. I busted my *tumbling* at Nationals. That means I screwed up. It wasn't bad, it didn't cost us the Worlds bid, but I started to like, obsess over my performance. My cardio time, my calorie intake, every second of training had to count. It just made me start to hate myself. Like, if I wasn't pushing myself as hard as I could, every single day, it wasn't good enough. And if it wasn't good enough, then *I* wasn't good enough. You don't know what it's like, James. Having everyone expect you to be perfect all the time. If you're not the best, you're not going to win, and if you're not winning, you're a loser.

JAMES: Thanks a lot, June.

JUNE: What? Anyway, it's not like I'm trying to excuse what I did. It was awful, I regretted it as soon as it happened. I'm just trying to explain. Kennedy is like the worst side of me, James. She's the me I could see myself becoming when I was in ACD the first time, and I hated her. She's afraid all the time, and it makes her act horrible! *(Beat).* I just—I didn't want that girl to be me. I wanted to show everybody that I'm different.

JAMES: Well, you did a pretty shit [bad] job.

JUNE: *(Tearing up:)* Yeah, I guess I did. *(Beat.)* God, that video has been up for days. Everybody probably hates me by now.

JAMES: It's got like five views so far. *(Beat.)* And I watched it five times.

JUNE: Why did you watch it?

JAMES: *(Embarrassed:)* Maybe I was missing you, and I got little desperate.

JUNE: Look, I'm sorry. I'm really, really sorry. I just want it to be like it was before. When we used to hang out every day, and it was just about having fun.

JAMES: I needed those times with you so bad. I was a fool to think you might like me. I'm not a winner like you, June. I'm a loser.

JUNE: You are *not* a —

JAMES: Yeah, I am. Nobody expects anything from me. My parents don't even care how I do in school, as long as I don't bug them for lunch money. Why do you think I always want to hang out at your house? We can't watch TV at mine, June. The sofa's taken. My dad's always drunk and that's where he sleeps it off. You know what I'm talking about.

JUNE: What? I didn't know it had gotten that bad. Why didn't you tell me? You always just change the subject when we get to your family.

JAMES: Well you like complaining about yours so much, I didn't want to interrupt!

JUNE: That's not fair! Maybe I should have paid more attention, but you can't just hide your feelings all the time and expect me to know what you need.

JAMES: Okay, well I'm telling you now. I needed you June. I still do.

JUNE: I need you too, James.

JAMES: I'm just not sure that's enough for me anymore.

(James exits. June waits a moment, stunned, and exits in the opposite direction.)

SCENE 4

(Backstage at Nationals. June enters furtively, dressed in her unitard with sweatpants over it, clutching a large makeup bag and a hand mirror. She looks around, doesn't see anyone, spies the folding chair and sits down. She grabs another folding chair and opens it to set her makeup bag on. She gets her foundation out and awkwardly puts it on while trying, unsuccessfully, to hold the mirror at the same time.)

(Barbara enters.)

BARBARA: Oh sweetie, here you are. Coach Kay was looking for you a minute ago. Why aren't you in the dressing room with all the other girls?

JUNE: I just wanted to get away from everybody for a moment, Mom.

BARBARA: Are you nervous?

JUNE: No, Mom! I need some space to get in the zone.

BARBARA: Okay, sure honey. *(Beat.)* Do you want me to leave?

JUNE: No...

(Barbara sits down in the other chair, holding the mirror up so that June can continue putting on her make-up.)

Thanks, that's really helpful. *(Beat.)* Mom, I have a question. *(Beat.)* Did you and Dad want me back in cheer because you were sick of having me around?

BARBARA: What? No, of course not. Why would you ever think that?

JUNE: You just seemed so mad at me all the time after I quit.

BARBARA: We weren't mad, honey. We were scared.

JUNE: Well, why were you *scared* at me all the time?

BARBARA: You are quite a formidable person, June. We never really know what you're going to do next. That's why it scared us so much when you did nothing for so long.

JUNE: I wasn't doing nothing! I was just hanging out, having fun. It was nice, for a while.

BARBARA: And then?

JUNE: Then I started to feel like, I don't know. I guess I started thinking about leaving for college, maybe, and having to be good at stuff again, having to care. It freaked me out. I don't really like not-caring. I just care too much.

BARBARA: Well you could always try caring too much about the people you're with, instead of the competition.

JUNE: I do!

BARBARA: I'm not trying to criticize you, June-y. I'm just saying that if the stakes feel too high when you focus so intensely on yourself and your own performance, you might try focusing on your teammates. Remember, you're not all alone out there. You're part of a team.

JUNE: Mom, I did something really awful.

BARBARA: I know.

JUNE: *(Genuinely shocked:)* You do?

BARBARA: I know you, June. Do you think I can't tell when you've done something you're not proud of? And I think I have a pretty good idea what it is, too.

JUNE: Mom, I feel so terrible. I let everybody down. What should I do?

BARBARA: That's up to you, sweetheart. But right now, there are some girls out there who need you. It's time to stop trying to *be* the best, and give *them* your best instead.

(Barbara exits. June stands up. She's had an epiphany and she exits with purpose.)

SCENE 5

(Backstage at Nationals. The ACD girls are near the front of center stage, some are on the mat behind. They stretch and mime conversation, with Kennedy, Gabi, Sam, Chrissy near the front watching the competition walk by.)

GABI: Oh my God. Can you believe Cheer Euphoria's new outfits? Pink leopard print with lime green shorts? Like anyone is going to take them seriously when they look like a bunch of 1991 Barbie doll panties.

KENNEDY: Their best tumbler is just as good as our clumsiest buster. Seriously, it's embarrassing to see them lose so hard year after year.

SAM: Don't look now but Cami Wilson just walked through the door. Her eyes look like a drugged pit bull.

KENNEDY: What a trainwreck. I heard she dropped a girl at Regionals.

CHRISSY: *(Wanting to join in:)* Yeah, Cami is so...not as good as she could be...at cheerleading...and make-up.

GABI: Woah! Here comes Austin Cheer Corps.

KENNEDY: Ladies, big smiles, show them our ACD hospitality.

ALL: *(Overlapping:)* Hey!
Good luck out there!
You guys look great!
Break legs!

(They watch as the group walks away.)

KENNEDY: What a bunch of freaks.

GABI: They didn't even smile back at us!

SAM: They're just jealous.

(Coach Jay walks up to the group.)

COACH JAY: You ladies wouldn't be acting like little catty cats right now, would you? You know we don't condone that kind of behavior at ACD.

SAM: Hey look, Beverly Christian from Cheer USA is here.

COACH JAY: I can't believe that horror show is still around! Her face is literal garbage.

(Jay moves off with the other girls to mime talking in a circle; Kay enters stage right and joins them. June enters with a determined look on her face.)

JUNE: Kennedy, hey, do you have a second?

KENNEDY: We're going on in 15 minutes.

JUNE: I know. I wouldn't interrupt you unless it was important.

(June moves away from the group to a spot downstage and Kennedy follows her.)

I owe you a huge apology.

KENNEDY: I knew it! I knew it was you. I don't need this right before we go on.

JUNE: Kennedy! Please. I understand if you never want to speak to me again. I just wanted to let you know, I'm not tumbling today.

KENNEDY: *(Shocked:)* What? Seriously?

JUNE: I think it would be better if you went last. I just told Coach Kay and she approved the switch. Plus, Cassidy got her full up to speed this week and I'd —

KENNEDY: But what about the scouts, what about the scholarship? I thought you were going for it? What about your parents?

JUNE: My parents will be okay. They just want me to be happy. I'm still going to give you some competition out there...but, I don't want it as much as you. You deserve a full ride in cheer, Kennedy. You deserve to go all the way. Honestly, all of us should be paying you to be at ACD. I've never met someone so determined to meet their goals in my entire life.

KENNEDY: Have you looked in a mirror lately?

JUNE: Thanks...I'll take that as a compliment. *(She smiles.)* Kennedy, we've got this. The team is in great shape, and that's thanks to you. Can we have a truce? Please?

(June offers her hand to Kennedy. Kennedy hesitates for a moment.)

KENNEDY: ...I'll admit, I haven't exactly been fair to you either. I know I pushed it a little too hard sometimes...Okay. Truce.

(They shake hands.)

But you better bring it out there, Davis, or I'll have you doing push-ups all the way to Worlds.

CHRISSY: Hey June and Kennedy! We go on in eight minutes!

(They join the group, along with Coach Kay who has just entered.)

JUNE: Do you mind if I...say something, Coach?

COACH KAY: Go ahead, but make it quick.

JUNE: I know I came in late to the game with a lot to make up for, and I didn't always have the best attitude about it. But you were my teammates, and you made me feel like part of the team. You guys have really been there for me. Thanks. For some of us, it's our last year in All-Star Cheerleading. For others, *(Looking at Kennedy:)* it's just the beginning. I don't know where I'll be in a year, but I know how much I love being right here, right now, with all of you. Let's leave everything else behind us—what our parents think, what we're doing after high school, even what we're doing later tonight. This is now. When we're on the mat, we know who we are. We're Austin Cheer Depot and we're here to support each other.

ALL: Aw.

JUNE: And kick butt of course!

(Laughter.)

Let's not forget who the most butt-kicking lady of us all is— our team captain, Kennedy Campbell. Kennedy, do you have anything to say?

KENNEDY: Yeah, I do. Guys, I know I don't really say this enough, but our team is killer. I got a little too focused on winning this year, and I've been too hard on you guys sometimes, maybe on myself, too. But I want you to know that I am absolutely amazed by every single one of you. We do things on that mat that other teenagers...hell, even other athletes could only dream about. We've been working hard and now it's time to play. Seriously, let's leave it all on the mat!

CHRISSY: *(Overcome with enthusiasm:)* YES!

KENNEDY: Hands in!

(They all put their hands in together. All smiling.)

Three, two, one —

ALL: Austin Cheer Depot!

(Letting the audience see a final routine is impressive but not necessary. There are some options for staging here: 1: They all exit in dim light and then begin to file out onstage in a line as a VO announces them, "Give it up for Austin Cheer Depot Senior Five!" The team executes the full climactic cheer sequence and Kennedy indeed goes last in the tumble box. After the routine is over the cheerleaders collapse and rejoice, hugging each other on the mat, before getting up and leaving together; 2: They all exit Scene 5 and we can hear a VO announcement in the distance, as if it is far away, "Give it up for Austin Cheer Depot Senior 5!" and we move almost immediately to Act II, Scene 6 [after a music transition and blackout to give the impression of a passage of time].)

SCENE 6

(The lights come up on a cluster center stage. The girls are backstage post-performance and awards ceremony. They are beaming. Kennedy holds onto a large trophy.)

GABI: We got the bid for Worlds, baby!

(Gabi high-fives Chrissy.)

CHRISSY: I didn't pass out! I didn't trip! I smiled the whole time! I am a cheer machine!

SAM: You are!

(Chrissy hugs Sam.)

CHRISSY: See, Sam! I knew you liked cheerleading! You haven't stopped grinning since we got off the mat!

SAM: It's the adrenaline!

GABI: Uh huh! Whatever!

JUNE: That felt *amazing*! You killed that pass, Kennedy!

KENNEDY: Thanks! Guess what? Coach Kay just told me that I have an interview with the scout from Louisville. I can't believe it! I'm gonna go to college! No one in my family has gone to college! My mom is gonna be so happy.

GABI: Hell yeah, girl!

JUNE: Are you happy?

KENNEDY: Are you kidding? I live for moments like this.

(Kennedy grabs June in a rough hug and June is happily surprised. June's parents walk on and June bounds over to them.)

JUNE: Mom, Dad!

BOB: Hey, sweetheart!

BARBARA: I couldn't stop crying, you all did such a good job!

BOB: She was holding my hand so tight I thought I was going to lose it.

JUNE: Oh my gosh! I loved it! I don't know if it was perfect, but it felt perfect. I can't wait for Worlds!

(James walks up sheepishly.)

Oh...can you guys hang out for a minute?

BOB: Sure, honey.

JUNE: James! You came to Dallas?

JAMES: Hey Junebug. Yeah, Mr. ComputerHands drove me. He's actually a pretty nice guy.

JUNE: Did you come to see Kennedy? She has AWESOME news!

JAMES: That's cool but, actually, I came to see you.

(He holds up a teddy bear with pom-poms and a little cheer uniform from behind his back.)

I got you something. *(Beat.)* I know you don't have pom-poms, but they didn't have a badass competitive cheerleader bear at Build-A-Bear.

JUNE: *(Hugging the bear:)* You built a bear for me?!

JAMES: I can't believe I never came to watch you compete before. That was awesome! That music mix was pure insanity and when everyone jumped at the same time—

(June hugs James suddenly and tightly.)

JUNE: I missed you so much, Jamie.

JAMES: I've missed you too.

JUNE: I've been thinking a lot about us...lately...and...I want you in my life. I'm not exactly sure what that means right now, but I'm willing to give things a try.

(She kisses him gently on the cheek and then grabs his hand, holding it.)

BARBARA: Looks like someone decided to kiss and make up.

BOB: Not a bad idea!

(Barbara and Bob hug each other and kiss. Coach Kay and Jay walk over to the center of the action. Kay looks ecstatic and Jay looks exhaustingly relieved.)

COACH KAY: We did it! We did it again, Jay. We pulled it out. Another championship notch in the wall.

COACH JAY: Ah! *(Sighs a huge sigh of relief.)* Cheeracles do happen!

(Coach Kay and Jay embrace and kiss, only to sputter and spit after doing so. The cheerleaders look on, whooping but also grossed out.)

Nope. Bad idea.

COACH KAY: Really bad idea.

(Curtain.)

The Authors Speak

What inspired you to write this play?

I met Halyn Lee Erickson, who was the inspiration for Kennedy Campbell in the script, in 2010. She is personally not very similar to Kennedy, but before becoming an improviser had cheered competitively for 13 years through a local gym, Austin Cheer Factory. She won innumerable national awards and competitions and ate, breathed, and dreamed of cheer. As a pre-teen, I had wanted to cheer at my middle school, but I didn't have the money or resources to be able to. I always found the sport of cheerleading fascinating, but when I saw what Halyn had done, the very athletic All-Star style of cheerleading, I was beyond intrigued. I fell down a rabbit hole into what All-Star cheerleading was. The various kinds of teams. The rivalries both inside and outside of the gyms. The level of athleticism required. The politics. The HAIR BOWS. It's a bizarre and beautiful world, with its own rules and etiquette. Around 2011 while I was painting for a month at the Vermont Studio Center, the idea for the show started coming into my head very strongly. I was listening to a podcast about the New Colony Theater Company in Chicago, Illinois. They use improvisation to develop their scripts and throughout their entire process. Unlike other devised work, they still leave certain lines or moments up to improvisation during the live performances. By all accounts, it leads to a very fresh and alive theatre experience. I had wanted to stage a cheerleading show, but originally it was going to be improvised. But did I really want to have choreographed routines along with an improvised plot? The mechanics would be difficult. But this New Colony style intrigued me. Plus, Halyn had told me that I could learn how to cheer, given enough time. She was a cheer coach on the side and had brought many adolescents up to cheer perfection in a matter of months. Also, I had a lot of talented performer friends who would be perfect for the show, and a very gifted writer friend Amy Gentry who loved teen comedies as much as I did. My husband is an incredible director and had agreed to work on the project. All of the actors playing the main cheerleader roles agreed to train for nine months in order to convincingly be in a full cheer routine. And then I booked a large enough venue, The Salvage Vanguard Theater, a warehouse space in East Austin. After everyone was on board, we started our improv sessions and our writing sessions and *Blood, Sweat, and Cheers* was born. (Kaci Beeler)

When Kaci approached me to co-write the script, I got really excited. I am a huge fan of movies like *Stick It* that are funny, but also show a respect for the sport and for female athletes. I thought, this is my chance to write a teen comedy that also has girls doing crazy stunts and flying through the air—I'm in! (Amy Gentry)

Was the structure or other elements of the play influenced by any other work?

I saw *Posh* on the West End in 2012, which features a large young male cast and a great stinger opening. The scene is set at the beginning with just a few characters and mostly quiet dialogue and then the stage peels back to reveal the large and energetic cast. The execution of the reveal was quick, loud, and unexpected. It was an exhilarating moment and I wanted the cheer gym reveal to feel the same way in *Blood, Sweat, and Cheers*. The story of the play is not so unlike *Mean Girls* or *Stick It* or any number of Bildungsroman plots. I love Young Adult fiction and I love a good underdog athletic story. It's fun and relatable! We were also very inspired by films like *Bridesmaids* and *Heathers*, which have large female-centric casts. It's our personal opinion that there are not enough large cast female comedies, and we wanted to utilize the female talent pool we had at our fingertips. The character of Coach Katherine Pepper also shares some rage-filled passion with the character of Sue Sylvester from *Glee*, but we only realized this in retrospect. (KB)

Have you dealt with the same theme in other works that you have written?

I have staged a few other improvised productions that focused on teenage protagonists and their coming-of-age stories. This includes *After School Improv* (2009), an improvised after-school special, *Reform School for Wayward Girls* (2014), and even our very popular *Charles Dickens Unleashed* (2009) show. These shows worked on similar themes of belonging, growing up, overcoming peer pressure, and acceptance. They also utilized a lot of comedic elements and didn't take themselves too seriously. (KB)

What writers have had the most profound effect on your style?

As a person who primarily improvises full-length plays onstage, I've learned to use my own point of view very strongly. My favorite thing to do in improvisation is to get into a character's mindset so firmly that I don't even have to think about what I'm saying. The character says and does everything. I'm just a passenger. Tina Fey and Amy Poehler have a very similar background to me, and I enjoy the way they both write and act. They write for their actors, and that's what I did. I knew who was playing what parts and I wrote the action and dialogue based on the strengths of my talented friends. Their voices were in my head when I was writing and it guided me in a lot of ways. I think the characters of Chrissy and Coach Jay most strongly represent what actors Kayla Freeman and Curtis Luciani brought to those roles. (KB)

What do you hope to achieve with this work?

My original goal with **Blood, Sweat, and Cheers** was to write and stage a piece of theatre that brought elements to the Austin theater scene that I had rarely witnessed. First, I wanted a comedy that felt genuine and fresh. Improvised dialogue always sounds natural but scripted dialogue rarely does. The New Colony process promised something that sounded like a solution to this. Second, All-Star cheerleading, as large as it is, is still a niche sport, and I wanted to shine a light on it. It was exhilarating to think of what it would be like to toss girls into the air in front of a live audience in a (relatively) small theater space. Third, while our improv comedy and scripted theatre communities in Austin get along pretty well, they are still very separate in a lot of ways. **BSC** was my chance to blend them, and I brought in designers and actors from both worlds to work together on the project.

My goal with putting this script out into the world is not so different, but it has changed. I want other people to enjoy this very fun show and world. I want young female actors to feel empowered in these roles and to enjoy the camaraderie that comes with a female-lead piece that is NOT about being a woman. (KB)

What were the biggest challenges involved in the writing of this play?

Well, we knew we could bring the comedy, all of the actors cast in the production had been winning local awards for comedy for years, but the real challenge was bringing heart and purpose to the piece. Amy and I wanted it to reflect real challenges young people face, and give the audience a strong story that they could care about while also enjoying the spectacle.

Also, writing the script together was a new challenge for both of us, and it was a great learning experience. We wanted our tones to match up, and for us to both fully understand the characters. The two of us were at all of the improv sessions, and knew the actors fairly well. We continued to tweak the script in the rehearsal process to make sure the characters felt like real people, even when they were acting ridiculously.

It's also a longer piece with a lot of characters and moving parts, and cutting scenes down after we created the first draft was a big challenge. We differed on a few ideas of what we wanted to keep or cut, but in the end we were able to come to a compromise on it. It was truly a collaborative piece between us, the director Roy Janik, and the actors. (KB)

What inspired you to become a playwright?

After I spent several years improvising plays, I realized that I had story, plot, character, theme, tone, genre, etc, all in my brain and my body. My main ensemble in Austin, TX is a small but mighty quartet called Parallelogramophonograph (or PGraph for short). We've been working together non-stop since 2005. Early on in our time together we realized that we all wanted to do improvised plays, but there weren't a lot of people or teachers around to help us hone that style. We have a weekly show in Austin (since 2006) so we spent literally years of trial and error in rehearsals and shows getting story into our bones. Once I have an idea of the characters, setting, and tone, I can jump into any story with relative ease, the main hurdle for me is being inspired to create and flesh out a new world and story. It's unlikely that I'll write something lengthy if I'm not also going to produce and stage it. I create the work that I want to exist in the world, plain and simple. Before **BSC**, I had written sketches, monologues, collaborative pieces, and shorter work, but **Blood, Sweat, and Cheers** was my first full-length scripted play. (KB)

How did you research the subject?

One of our actors and cheer coach, Halyn Lee Erickson, had lived in the world of All-Star Cheer, so our lengthy discussions and interviews together helped Amy and I a lot. We also visited Austin Cheer Factory, Halyn's childhood training center, and watched several practices. I should also mention that there are hundreds of great videos of routines and guides online, including a documentary about the California All-Stars cheer squad called *The Cheerleaders*, produced by AwesomenessTV. And of course, everyone can watch the Olympics of cheer, The Cheerleading Worlds Championship, on ESPN every Spring. (KB)

Are any characters modeled after real life or historical figures?

The character of James Kowalski (played originally by actor Alex Dobrenko) was very similar to boys that Amy and I had been friends with when we were younger. The experience of a platonic relationship that starts to become something else was something we both understood and wanted to portray. It was important to us that the central relationship of the story be more realistic to the awkwardness of real teenage relationships. Honestly, a lot of the characters are archetypes of people I think a lot of us have known or met before. The well-meaning but completely clueless parents. The intense but vastly misunderstood bully. The sweet and lovably dopey kid with a heart of gold. The unflappable older girl who has it all figured it. These were also tiny personalities of the original actors that were blown up to an extreme level for the characters. There is a kernel of truth to every one of them. (KB)

How was the first production different from the vision that you created in your mind?

There were a lot of moving parts in this piece, and so the full production was a lot bigger in some ways than my original idea. When everyone was backstage before the show, and it was very crowded, I realized how many people had to come together to make this thing real. It's no small effort to make live theatre, and all of the little quirks and changes along the way are something to embrace and learn from. At some point, it's too late to change the script, and you just have to enjoy what is happening right in front of you. (Kaci Beeler)

About the Authors

Kaci Beeler is a visual artist, improviser, writer, and stage and film actor based out of Austin, TX. She has been performing improvisational theatre since 2002 and is a company member with several award-winning ensembles including Parallelogramophonograph and Available Cupholders. In addition to her acting work, Kaci has created, directed, and produced dozens of improvised and devised shows in Austin and has won several Austin Critics Table and Austin Chronicle "Best of Austin" Awards. She has presented original productions at Austin's internationally renowned Fusebox Festival and the Edinburgh Fringe Festival and has toured to over 40 cities and seven countries to perform and teach others how to improvise full-length plays on the spot. Her work has been published in several anthologies and periodicals including the *Austin Chronicle, Saveur Magazine*, and *Time Out New York*.

Amy Gentry is a writer living in Austin, Texas. As a sketch comedian, she has performed in Austin Sketchfest, the Out of Bounds Comedy Festival, and the Encyclopedia Show. Her freelance writing can be found in the *Chicago Tribune, Austin Chronicle, LA Review of Books, xoJane, The Hairpin*, and others. She holds a PhD in English.

About YouthPLAYS

YouthPLAYS (www.youthplays.com) is a publisher of award-winning professional dramatists and talented new discoveries, each with an original theatrical voice, and all dedicated to expanding the vocabulary of theatre for young actors and audiences. On our website you'll find one-act and full-length plays and musicals for teen and pre-teen (and even college) actors, as well as duets and monologues for competition. Many of our authors' works have been widely produced at high schools and middle schools, youth theatres and other TYA companies, both amateur and professional, as well as at elementary schools, camps, churches and other institutions serving young audiences and/or actors worldwide. Most are intended for performance by young people, while some are intended for adult actors performing for young audiences.

YouthPLAYS was co-founded by professional playwrights Jonathan Dorf and Ed Shockley. It began merely as an additional outlet to market their own works, which included a substantial body of award-winning published and unpublished plays and musicals. Those interested in their published plays were directed to the respective publishers' websites, and unpublished plays were made available in electronic form. But when they saw the desperate need for material for young actors and audiences—coupled with their experience that numerous quality plays for young people weren't finding a home—they made the decision to represent the work of other playwrights as well. Dozens and dozens of authors are now members of the YouthPLAYS family, with scripts available both electronically and in traditional acting editions. We continue to grow as we look for exciting and challenging plays and musicals for young actors and audiences.

About ProduceaPlay.com

Let's put up a play! Great idea! But producing a play takes time, energy and knowledge. While finding the necessary time and energy is up to you, ProduceaPlay.com is a website designed to assist you with that third element: knowledge.

Created by YouthPLAYS' co-founders, Jonathan Dorf and Ed Shockley, ProduceaPlay.com serves as a resource for producers at all levels as it addresses the many facets of production. As Dorf and Shockley speak from their years of experience (as playwrights, producers, directors and more), they are joined by a group of award-winning theatre professionals and experienced teachers from the world of academic theatre, all making their expertise available for free in the hope of helping this and future generations of producers, whether it's at the school or university level, or in community or professional theatres.

The site is organized into a series of major topics, each of which has its own page that delves into the subject in detail, offering suggestions and links for further information. For example, Publicity covers everything from Publicizing Auditions to How to Use Social Media to Posters to whether it's worth hiring a publicist. Casting details Where to Find the Actors, How to Evaluate a Resume, Callbacks and even Dealing with Problem Actors. You'll find guidance on your Production Timeline, The Theater Space, Picking a Play, Budget, Contracts, Rehearsing the Play, The Program, House Management, Backstage, and many other important subjects.

The site is constantly under construction, so visit often for the latest insights on play producing, and let it help make your play production dreams a reality.

More from YouthPLAYS

The Adventures of Rocky & Skye by Kelly DuMar
Comedy. 30-35 minutes. 2-16 males, 2-21 females (4-37 performers possible).

A quartet of characters grow up before our eyes, as we witness the friendship, fun and social skirmishes they encounter on their journey from kindergarten through middle school. Whether they're debating whose father can reach the moon first, kissing and telling, picturing unlikely future careers, double dating or waiting for the last bell of middle school to ring, they'll inspire us to laugh and appreciate the extraordinary moments of ordinary life.

Choose Your Own Oz by Tommy Jamerson
Comedy. 85-100 minutes. 4-15+ females, 4-15+ males (10-30+ performers possible).

The Wizard of Oz meets *Choose Your Own Adventure* in this fresh and fast-paced retelling of the L. Frank Baum classic in which the audience plays playwright and gets the chance to change everything from Dorothy's footwear (silver slippers or ruby red...clown shoes?) to Toto's species (lion, tiger or octopus?—oh my!) to the Witch's flying footmen. A delight for children of all ages, *Choose Your Own Oz* reminds us all that at the end of the day, there really is no place like home.

Exposure by Vishesh Abeyratne
Drama. 35-45 minutes. 3-4 females, 3-4 males (7 performers).

Jenna just can't seem to remember the details of her first wild party. But when her best friend uploads a scandalous video of her drunken exploits online, the memories come flooding back all too vividly. As the embarrassing footage makes its way through cyberspace, will the mistakes of one night change the lives of Jenna and her friends forever?

Sleepy Hollow by Elizabeth Doyle (music), Judy Freed (book), Owen Kalt (lyrics)

Musical Comedy. 90 minutes (may be cut down to a 60-minute version). 6+ males, 5+ females (11+ performers possible).

A scheming schoolmaster. An apprehensive heiress. A restless ghost with a penchant for decapitation. And a teenage girl who thinks demons are delightful. Nothing is as it seems in this fresh, funny adaptation of Washington Irving's classic American tale, *The Legend of Sleepy Hollow*.

The Tea Servant by Ed Shockley

Drama. 30-35 minutes. 3+ males, 2+ females (5-25 performers possible).

Adapted from an anonymous Samurai legend, **The Tea Servant** is the tale of a serving girl whose impetuous princess is determined to travel alone to her lover. The servant dresses as a samurai to discourage robbers, but she is no fighter. When confronted on the road by a highwayman, the servant asks for time to deliver her mistress safe to the village and promises to return to duel. And when she does, her courage in facing death gains her far more than she could have imagined.

Aesop Refabled by Nicole B. Adkins, Jeff Goode, Adam Hahn, Samantha Macher, Liz Shannon Miller, Dominic Mishler, Mike Rothschild and Dave Ulrich

Comedy. 45-60 minutes. 3-11 males, 3-11 females (3-21 performers possible).

One of L.A.'s edgiest theatre companies brings a modern spin to Aesop's classic yarns, as eight timeless fables get a 21st century reboot. Cupcake bullies, tween warriors, scheming cheerleaders and apocalyptic yellow butterfly people... Each tale takes an unexpected twist in this innovative offering!

Made in the USA
Columbia, SC
22 December 2021